BERNARD MAGEE'S
BRIDGE
QUIZ BOOK

BERNARD MAGEE'S
BRIDGE
QUIZ BOOK

Bernard Magee

First published as *Collins Bridge Quiz Book* in 1996 by
CollinsWillow, an imprint of HarperCollins*Publishers.*

Copyright © **Mr Bridge**
Text © Bernard Magee

This edition published in 2009 by
Mr Bridge
Ryden Grange
Knaphill
Surrey
GU21 2TH

The moral right of the author has been asserted.

ISBN 1 85665 026 X

A CIP catalogue record for this book is available from the British Library.

Type-set by Ruth Edmondson, Saltash, Cornwall.
Printed by The Magazine Printing Company, Brimsdown, Middlesex

CONTENTS

INTRODUCTION

This book aims at entertaining everybody who knows anything about bridge. To that end, it is filled with questions and quizzes – 81 full-page bridge problems and 164 trivia questions. It is divided into nine chapters, each containing a variety of questions on declarer play, defence, bidding, opening leads and trivia.

Bernard Magee's Bridge Quiz Book is designed to appeal to everybody's tastes, flitting between strong and weak no-trump, and even delving into the exotic in the conventions chapter. Other than in the last chapter, the bridge problems are each laid out on a full page with the answer on the page immediately following; clear layouts accompany both question and answer – it is all designed for your ease and pleasure. The answers to the trivia quizzes are similarly given on the following page.

There should be something for everyone, especially in the trivia sections which are jam-packed with questions on every aspect of the game. It is hoped that you will get hours of pleasure and enjoyment from these pages and learn something new at the same time.

Mr Bridge

Chapter 1

Rubber Bridge

The oldest and most popular form of bridge, enjoyed by gamblers and socialites alike. The bidding tends to be pure (not infected by conventions) and the play centres around the making of contracts. Undertricks and overtricks tend to be neglected – indeed, too much thought in this area is considered downright anti-social. Bid to game and make it and you will be a big winner!

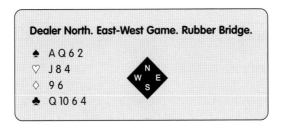

Dealer North. East-West Game. Rubber Bridge.

♠ A Q 6 2
♡ J 8 4
♢ 9 6
♣ Q 10 6 4

South	West	North	East
		1♡	Pass
3NT	All Pass		

3NT could be anything – either simply hogging the hand or perhaps a solid minor with suits stopped, or 13–15 with 4-3-3-3 shape. Herein lies the essence of Rubber Bridge – allowed to act on their instinct, those with inbred 'card sense' tend to be the best Rubber Bridge players. That is not to say that there is no science to the bidding, but it is also related to the personalities of the players at the table.

What should West lead?

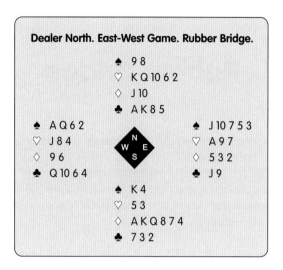

Dealer North. East-West Game. Rubber Bridge.

	♠ 9 8	
	♡ K Q 10 6 2	
	◇ J 10	
	♣ A K 8 5	

♠ A Q 6 2		♠ J 10 7 5 3
♡ J 8 4		♡ A 9 7
◇ 9 6		◇ 5 3 2
♣ Q 10 6 4		♣ J 9

	♠ K 4	
	♡ 5 3	
	◇ A K Q 8 7 4	
	♣ 7 3 2	

South	West	North	East
		1♡	Pass
3NT	All Pass		

What lead will declarer expect? Surely the most popular lead against such contracts is the unbid major, and thus this is the most likely suit for South to have stopped. This is not solid logic, but many times you will find it holds true; just think about your own bidding when sometimes you bid 3NT because you think you know what the lead will be.

Here South bids 3NT, not giving anything away in the auction, and fully expects a spade lead – that makes seven tricks and surely partner can supply two more.

A club is likely to be safest against this type of hand, and also against the balanced hands, as it is less likely to give a trick away; with five spades, the balance would swing back to a spade lead, but with only four, it is best to rely on partner having an entry, which he will use to play a spade through declarer.

A club works best on this hand, holding declarer to seven or eight tricks. Partner will not let a heart slip by him and a spade switch will be obvious, netting six tricks and two down.

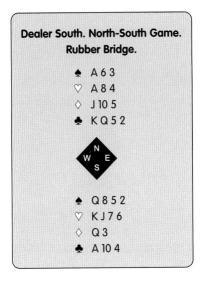

Dealer South. North-South Game.
Rubber Bridge.

♠ A 6 3
♡ A 8 4
◇ J 10 5
♣ K Q 5 2

♠ Q 8 5 2
♡ K J 7 6
◇ Q 3
♣ A 10 4

South	West	North	East
1NT¹	Pass	3NT	All Pass

¹weak no-trump (12–14)

West leads the ◇4 to the ◇K and the
◇9 is returned to the ◇Q, West playing the ◇2.

It is often right to lead a major suit when the opponents have failed to use Stayman, but such an idea has not deterred West from finding the best lead.

We are playing Rubber Bridge so there is no need to search for overtricks. The contract's security is the number one priority. It seems that there are three more diamond tricks to lose so we need nine tricks before losing another one. Where should we start and which way should we head?

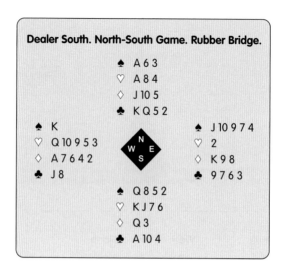

Dealer South. North-South Game. Rubber Bridge.

```
            ♠ A 6 3
            ♥ A 8 4
            ◇ J 10 5
            ♣ K Q 5 2
♠ K                         ♠ J 10 9 7 4
♥ Q 10 9 5 3      N         ♥ 2
◇ A 7 6 4 2    W   E        ◇ K 9 8
♣ J 8             S         ♣ 9 7 6 3
            ♠ Q 8 5 2
            ♥ K J 7 6
            ◇ Q 3
            ♣ A 10 4
```

South	West	North	East
1NT¹	Pass	3NT	All Pass

¹weak no-trump (12–14)

West leads the ◇4 to the ◇K and the
◇9 is returned to the ◇Q, West playing the ◇2.

This could be rather important. A major-suit lead would have made life much easier (and most would probably have chosen one), but we still have plenty of chances, even though we cannot afford to lose the lead.

A finesse is available in both clubs and hearts, but in a game like this we should play for every chance, however slim.

Cash the ace of spades first, just in case, and of course this happens to be that case! The king falls and we can pick up two tricks from spades. Now we only need one more trick. Is it just a choice of finesses? No it certainly is not, for we have the chance of a doubleton jack of clubs or a doubleton queen of hearts, but most importantly we also have the chance of a 3-3 club break. So test clubs first and, lo and behold, down falls the jack and in comes our game with both finesses offside.

In Rubber Bridge (or Teams) when a game is tight, it is usually most important to try everything to make it, whereas in Pairs sometimes it is not just the overtricks that matter, but the undertricks too. Cashing the ace of spades at Pairs would have been dangerous for it would most likely cost an extra trick.

Dealer South. North-South Game.
Rubber Bridge.

```
        ♠ 7 6
        ♡ 7 6 4
        ◇ 10 9 8 3
        ♣ A K Q 10
                        ♠ 9 5 3
              N         ♡ Q J 10 8
           W     E      ◇ K 5 4
              S         ♣ 9 4 2
```

South	West	North	East
1◇	1♠	2◇	2♠
2NT¹	Pass	3NT	All Pass

¹18–19 points (balanced)

West leads the ♠Q, which holds,
then the ♠J which declarer wins with the ♠K.

A full-blooded natural 2NT call pushed the auction to a quick close and dummy comes down with plenty to spare.

What is the plan?

A

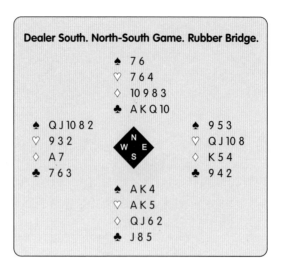

Dealer South. North-South Game. Rubber Bridge.

```
                      ♠ 7 6
                      ♡ 7 6 4
                      ◇ 10 9 8 3
                      ♣ A K Q 10
        ♠ Q J 10 8 2                      ♠ 9 5 3
        ♡ 9 3 2              N            ♡ Q J 10 8
        ◇ A 7           W         E       ◇ K 5 4
        ♣ 7 6 3              S            ♣ 9 4 2
                      ♠ A K 4
                      ♡ A K 5
                      ◇ Q J 6 2
                      ♣ J 8 5
```

South	West	North	East
1◇	1♠	2◇	2♠
2NT¹	Pass	3NT	All Pass

¹18–19 points (balanced)

West leads the ♠Q, which holds,
then the ♠J which declarer wins with the ♠K.

Partner has a maximum of seven points, three of which we have seen (queen and jack of spades). What four points can we give him that will let us take this contract down?

If partner has a top heart, declarer will surely be able to establish sufficient tricks in diamonds for his contract.

Our only chance is that partner holds the ace of diamonds and has at least two cards in the suit. Now that we have worked this out, we should be on our toes and ready to jump on the first diamond lead, winning it whilst still being able to lead a spade.

Declarer wins the second spade, crosses to dummy in clubs and leads a small diamond. We leap up with the king and play our final spade. Declarer wins but still has to lose the ace of diamonds and two more spades for one down.

Note, if partner wins the first diamond and plays a third spade, when we win the king of diamonds we will have no spades left. Be prepared!

Dealer South. East-West Game.
Rubber Bridge.

♠ A K 4 3
♡ A K 7
◇ J 6 2
♣ 9 7 4

♠ 8 6
♡ Q 6 3
◇ A Q 7 5
♣ A Q J 3

South	West	North	East
1NT¹	Pass	2♣	Pass
2◇	Pass	3NT	All Pass

¹strong no-trump (15–17)

West leads the ♠Q.

With a maximum of 32 points and such uninviting shape, North was happy to settle in an easy (?) 3NT. Had he found an eight-card spade fit he might have looked for a slam.

So, 30 points, surely this is going to be easy? Seven top tricks and plenty of high cards in the minors. Can we make certain of our contract?

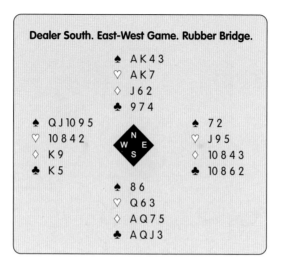

Dealer South. East-West Game. Rubber Bridge.

	♠ A K 4 3	
	♡ A K 7	
	◊ J 6 2	
	♣ 9 7 4	
♠ Q J 10 9 5		♠ 7 2
♡ 10 8 4 2		♡ J 9 5
◊ K 9		◊ 10 8 4 3
♣ K 5		♣ 10 8 6 2
	♠ 8 6	
	♡ Q 6 3	
	◊ A Q 7 5	
	♣ A Q J 3	

South	West	North	East
1NT¹	Pass	2♣	Pass
2◊	Pass	3NT	All Pass

¹strong no-trump (15–17)

West leads the ♠Q.

The only danger is a 5-2 spade break, making it possible to lose two minor suit kings and three spade tricks. So, assuming the worst (spades 5-2), we should duck the first round so that East will be out of spades if we lose a minor suit king to his hand.

We need two extra tricks, but we must avoid West getting the lead twice. That may not be easy – if West holds both minor kings we cannot help it, but can we establish two tricks by losing to only one king?

That is the crunch: we have to make West play his king on thin air and so we need to lead up to an honour in dummy and the jack of diamonds is the only one there.

So win the second round of spades, cash the ace of diamonds and lead a small diamond towards dummy. If West hops in with the king we have two more diamond tricks, but if West ducks, we can simply switch to clubs and establish the ninth trick there. Of course, if East had held the king of diamonds all along, he can do no harm, for he has no spades left.

There are many other possible lines of play, but none of them are failsafe like the 100% method outlined above.

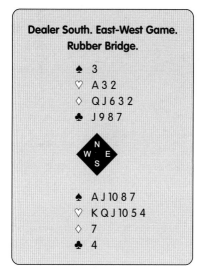

Dealer South. East-West Game.
Rubber Bridge.

♠ 3
♡ A 3 2
♢ Q J 6 3 2
♣ J 9 8 7

♠ A J 10 8 7
♡ K Q J 10 5 4
♢ 7
♣ 4

South	West	North	East
1♡[1]	Pass	2♡	Double
4♡	All Pass		

[1]five-card major

West leads the ♡8.

Once South had found support, he did not think twice about bidding game. And with two ruffs in dummy, game would have been odds on, but unfortunately the defence are being mean and have set out to foil that plan.

Realistically, we can hope for only one ruff in dummy because we have no entry back to hand and the defence will play a second trump when in. So how are we going to make 4♡ with only one ruff?

A

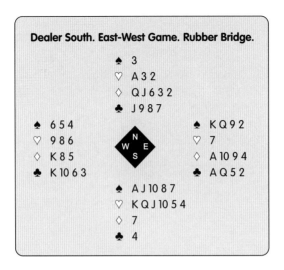

Dealer South. East-West Game. Rubber Bridge.

```
              ♠ 3
              ♡ A 3 2
              ◇ Q J 6 3 2
              ♣ J 9 8 7
   ♠ 6 5 4                    ♠ K Q 9 2
   ♡ 9 8 6          N          ♡ 7
   ◇ K 8 5      W       E      ◇ A 10 9 4
   ♣ K 10 6 3        S         ♣ A Q 5 2
              ♠ A J 10 8 7
              ♡ K Q J 10 5 4
              ◇ 7
              ♣ 4
```

South	West	North	East
1♡¹	Pass	2♡	Double
4♡	All Pass		

¹five-card major

West leads the ♡8.

We need to restrict our spade losers to one, but can only ruff once, because the defence will have little trouble drawing dummy's last trump when we have to yield the lead in a minor. From the bidding, it is likely that the spades break 4-3. So what chances do we have? Clearly if one hand holds ♠KQx then we can make by ruffing once and giving away one trick, but this is unlikely – is there anything better?

The best line is to win the trump in dummy and finesse in spades straight away – this is successful whenever East holds the king and queen, when West has three spades with the king and queen or when East holds three spades including an honour. Yes, East is more likely to hold four spades because of his double, but there is still that chance.

Win the ace of hearts, and play a spade to the jack which holds the trick! Now we take a spade ruff in dummy and try the queen of diamonds, but East lets this run to his partner's king so that he can return the expected trump. We win in dummy, ruff a diamond high and draw the last trump. Now we cash the ace of spades felling East's queen and exit with a fourth spade. East wins and cashes a club, but that is all.

At Rubber Bridge, very few conventions are allowed; Stayman, Blackwood and a defence to pre-empts, but little else. Of course, any four players can agree to play as many conventions as they wish, but the norm is for completely 'natural' bridge. It makes for much purer auctions. Try these problems:

(1) Dealer North. Love All.

♠ 6 3
♡ K Q 5 4 2
♢ K Q 6 3
♣ 7 2

South	West	North	East
		1NT¹	2♠
?			

¹weak no-trump (12–14)

(2) Dealer North. Game All.

♠ 7 2
♡ K Q 10 6 3
♢ K 10 9 2
♣ 3 2

South	West	North	East
		1NT¹	Pass
?			

¹strong no-trump (15–17)

(3) Dealer North. Love All.

♠ Q 4
♡ K 5 4 3
♢ K J 5
♣ Q 10 3 2

South	West	North	East
		1♠	2♢
?			

(4) Dealer North. Love All.

♠ 5
♡ 6 4 3
♢ 6 4 3
♣ A Q 8 5 3 2

South	West	North	East
		2♡	Pass
?			

(5) Dealer South. Love All.

♠ 6
♡ K Q 5 4 3 2
♢ A K 5
♣ K Q 5

South	West	North	East
1♡	1♠	3♡	3♠
?			

(1) 3♡ – No take-out double available nor a non-natural 2NT. In these kinds of auctions, there is not often room to differentiate between competitive and invitational hands. Here we are on the borderline between the two and if partner turns up with only two hearts and twelve points, we will be in the wrong place, but that is a risk we should take. After all if partner has fourteen points, game should be a good prospect, especially if there is a heart fit.

(2) 2♣ then 3♡ – With no transfers, it is a matter of knowing what is 'natural'. To differentiate between the various hands, Stayman is employed. With a weak hand, we bid our suit at the two level; with a strong hand, we bid our suit at the three level and with an intermediate hand, we bid Stayman first and then rebid our suit at the three level. This intermediate sequence invites opener to bid game. If opener shows a four-card heart suit in response to Stayman (2♡), then 4♡ should be a very good contract and that is what we should bid.

(3) 2NT – It is refreshing to be able to bid our hand so easily. Eleven points, balanced and a good stop in the enemy suit; what more could we ask for? There is no urgency to show four hearts; the more important part of a Rubber Bridge auction is to make the most descriptive bid and 2NT is certainly that. After all, partner can introduce a four-card suit over 2NT if he so wishes.

(4) 3♡ – Always try hard to support the strong two-bidder's suit. Here with three-card support and good ruffing values, we do not have to try very hard! The 3♡ bid usually promises one first-round control and this hand also fits that bill. 3♣ would simply take up space and belie the hand, for, of course, we are not strong enough for any positive call other than 3♡.

(5) 4NT (Blackwood) – Do not be put off by the intervening bids, partner's 3♡ bid is a sound raise, not pre-emptive, and so, with our strong and shapely hand, we are within our rights to hope for two aces and a small slam. Change a heart to a spade (giving us two potential spade losers) and it would be a different matter. Two aces would not be enough; we might still have two spade losers and hence it would be unwise to roll out Blackwood.

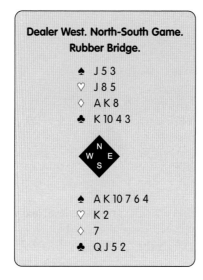

**Dealer West. North-South Game.
Rubber Bridge.**

♠ J 5 3
♡ J 8 5
◇ A K 8
♣ K 10 4 3

```
    N
 W     E
    S
```

♠ A K 10 7 6 4
♡ K 2
◇ 7
♣ Q J 5 2

South	West	North	East
	Pass	1NT[1]	4♡
4♠	All Pass		

[1]weak no-trump (12–14)

West leads the ♡3 to East's ♡A.

A nice and quick auction to what is surely the best spot. At this vulnerability, we would need to take 4♡ off four to beat making 4♠. But are we going to make 4♠?

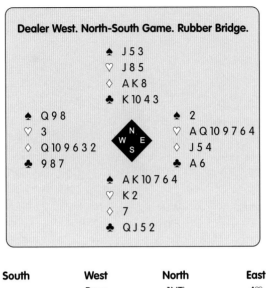

Dealer West. North-South Game. Rubber Bridge.

```
                    ♠ J 5 3
                    ♡ J 8 5
                    ◇ A K 8
                    ♣ K 10 4 3
    ♠ Q 9 8                       ♠ 2
    ♡ 3              N            ♡ A Q 10 9 7 6 4
    ◇ Q 10 9 6 3 2  W   E        ◇ J 5 4
    ♣ 9 8 7            S          ♣ A 6
                    ♠ A K 10 7 6 4
                    ♡ K 2
                    ◇ 7
                    ♣ Q J 5 2
```

South	West	North	East
	Pass	1NT¹	4♡
4♠	All Pass		

¹weak no-trump (12–14)

West leads the ♡3 to East's ♡A.

The key to this hand is the opening trick. It is quite clear that West has led a singleton and, if we follow with the two, the play to the first three tricks is likely to be ace of hearts, heart ruff, club ace, and now another heart would take us down if West started with Qxx or Qxxx in trumps. This is quite likely because East holds seven hearts so West is likely to hold longer spades.

What happens if we play the king of hearts at trick one? East is likely to think his partner has ♡32 doubleton and will surely switch. He would expect declarer to ruff his queen which would establish dummy's jack. It does appear that this play is likely to work and if it doesn't, we will just have to congratulate the East who outplayed us.

East is most likely to switch to a diamond. We win, cash the second top diamond throwing our heart and draw two rounds of trumps. We can only lose the ace of clubs and queen of spades now for ten tricks.

If trumps were 4-0, we would play similarly, but after the ace of spades shows up the bad break, we would lead up to the jack. If West wins the queen and plays a club to the ace, we can ruff the heart return high and then draw trumps with the jack and ten.

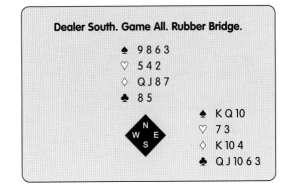

Dealer South. Game All. Rubber Bridge.

```
            ♠ 9 8 6 3
            ♡ 5 4 2
            ◇ Q J 8 7
            ♣ 8 5
                           ♠ K Q 10
              N            ♡ 7 3
            W   E          ◇ K 10 4
              S            ♣ Q J 10 6 3
```

South	West	North	East
2♡	Pass	2NT¹	Pass
3♡	Pass	4♡	All Pass

¹negative

West leads the ♣K, which holds and switches to a trump.

Declarer plays two rounds of trumps (all following) and then plays the six of diamonds to the two, queen and ...

The strong two was forcing and thus 2NT was a negative. We know little about South's hand except that he should hold eight playing tricks – surely six hearts and two aces?

Plan the defence.

A

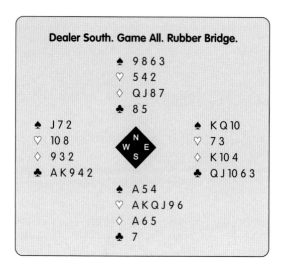

Dealer South. Game All. Rubber Bridge.

```
              ♠ 9 8 6 3
              ♡ 5 4 2
              ◇ Q J 8 7
              ♣ 8 5
♠ J 7 2                      ♠ K Q 10
♡ 10 8          N            ♡ 7 3
◇ 9 3 2      W     E         ◇ K 10 4
♣ A K 9 4 2     S            ♣ Q J 10 6 3
              ♠ A 5 4
              ♡ A K Q J 9 6
              ◇ A 6 5
              ♣ 7
```

South	West	North	East
2♡	Pass	2NT¹	Pass
3♡	Pass	4♡	All Pass

¹negative

West leads the ♣K, which holds and switches to a trump.

Declarer plays two rounds of trumps (all following) and then plays the six of diamonds to the two, queen and …

Partner should give count when declarer leads a key suit, and so his two of diamonds (lowest card) suggests an odd number (probably three). If we win, declarer will have three diamond tricks which by our estimates will be enough for his game, so it must be right to hold up (note that declarer cannot get to table in trumps because dummy's hearts are too small).

But that is only half the job! Declarer wins the queen of diamonds and ruffs a club back to hand. He cashes the ace of spades and we are ready (having made a plan!) to drop our king of spades underneath it. If declarer has the jack of spades we can do nothing – we still win two spade tricks, but are then endplayed, having to give up a third trick in diamonds or a ruff and discard – but if partner has the jack of spades he can now win the second spade and play a diamond through dummy breaking up the endplay.

Phew! Glad you made a plan?

Bernard Magee's Bridge Quiz Book

Q

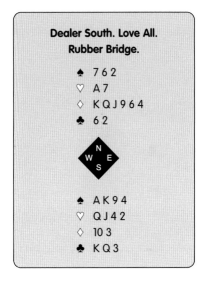

Dealer South. Love All.
Rubber Bridge.

- ♠ 7 6 2
- ♡ A 7
- ◇ K Q J 9 6 4
- ♣ 6 2

- ♠ A K 9 4
- ♡ Q J 4 2
- ◇ 10 3
- ♣ K Q 3

South	West	North	East
1NT	Pass	3NT	All Pass

West leads the ♣5 to the ♣A; East switches to the ♡K.

The bidding always seems so much more simple at Rubber Bridge! South opens a strong no-trump (15-17) and North happily raises to game (not a thought to the diamond suit).

This all looks rather easy, especially when East puts up his ace of clubs. Ready for a quick claim we are taken aback by East's king of hearts – the last card we expected and a rather awkward one at that. Dummy's diamonds are suddenly looking redundant.

What now?

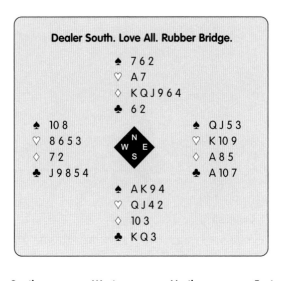

Dealer South. Love All. Rubber Bridge.

	North	
♠	7 6 2	
♡	A 7	
◇	K Q J 9 6 4	
♣	6 2	

West		East
♠ 10 8		♠ Q J 5 3
♡ 8 6 5 3		♡ K 10 9
◇ 7 2		◇ A 8 5
♣ J 9 8 5 4		♣ A 10 7

	South	
♠	A K 9 4	
♡	Q J 4 2	
◇	10 3	
♣	K Q 3	

South	West	North	East
1NT	Pass	3NT	All Pass

West leads the ♣5 to the ♣A; East switches to the ♡K.

We have seven top tricks and another one to come in the diamond suit (the defence will have to duck once). The obvious extra chance is a 3-3 spade break, but we would like better odds than that. There is just a chance that we will be able to endplay the defender with the longer diamonds, forcing him to lead a diamond to give dummy the last trick.

Win the ace of hearts and play a diamond to the ten, West playing the seven to show an even number, and now a second diamond which East wins, sending back a club. We win this, play the ace of spades (there might be extra chances if an honour falls) then duck a spade so that we can test the suit; another club comes back. Now we cash the king of spades, but East turns up with four; although this is bad news, there is still a glimmer of hope. We have to fall back on the second plan – East seems to have four spades, three diamonds, three clubs, one heart and two other cards – if his other two cards are hearts our plan should work.

Cash the queen and jack of hearts, East following to both of them, and with only two cards left, we know that East holds one spade and one diamond. Hence we can happily lead a spade for East to win and he, unhappily, has to lead a diamond to dummy. Nine tricks.

After such an inspirational play of the king of hearts, one has to feel rather sorry for East!

Q BRIDGE TRIVIA

1. Where is the trump suit usually placed in dummy?
2. What is a Kibitzer?
3. Playing Rubber Bridge, who shuffles the cards and where should they be placed?
4. What is a 'Book'?
5. What is the bonus for a small slam when vulnerable?
6. What is a Goulash?
7. How many different game contracts are there (assuming no partscore and excluding slam contracts)?
8. From which country is movie star and expert bridge player Omar Sharif?
9. What do you score for holding four aces in a no-trump contract at Rubber Bridge?
10. When all the cards to a trick have been played and turned face down, is one still allowed to check the trick?
11. Stakes in Rubber Bridge are expressed as a certain amount per point, but this has a different meaning on either side of the Atlantic. What is the difference?
12. Which is the odd one out: Portland, Schenken, Cavendish, Crockfords or Hamilton?
13. What are the odds against holding a Yarborough?
14. What is a Chukker (with respect to Contract Bridge)?
15. Which players are allowed to 'cut' the pack before the deal?
16. When was the Culbertson-Lenz match (labelled 'The Bridge Battle of the Century')?
17. What is the most one can theoretically score 'below the line' in one hand?
18. What happens after a passed-out hand in Chicago Bridge?
19. What does 'Weak and Double' mean when sitting down with an unknown at a Rubber Bridge table?
20. Who is responsible for the score at a Rubber Bridge table?

A ANSWERS TO BRIDGE TRIVIA

1. On dummy's right-hand side.

2. A spectator of bridge (and other sports); derived from the name of an inquisitive bird.

3. The dealer's partner, and they should be placed on his (her) right.

4. The first six tricks taken by the declarer's side, after which tricks count against the number contracted for.

5. 750.

6. A method of dealing for which the cards are not properly shuffled, and are then distributed five at a time to each player (twice) and then three at a time. This tends to lead to wildly distributional hands and is often a practice employed after a passed out hand at Rubber Bridge.

7. 50 (twenty-three redoubled, eighteen doubled and nine normal).

8. Egypt.

9. 150 points above the line.

10. Yes, in Rubber Bridge, but no, in Duplicate Bridge.

11. In Britain, a pound a point means a pound for every 100 points scored, but in America a dollar a point would mean exactly that and would be rather higher stakes – just picking up honours would be worth 100 dollars!

12. Schenken – it is a club system, the others are or were famous card clubs.

13. 1827 to one.

14. It is a set of four deals in Chicago Bridge.

15. Only the player to the right of dealer. Other players may request another cut, but it is the same player who repeats the task.

16. Between December 1931 and January 1932.

17. 880 (for 7NT redoubled) – all bonuses go above the line.

18. The hand is redealt by the same player – in normal Rubber Bridge, the deal passes to the next player.

19. It is a summary of the convention to be played; denoting a weak no-trump and a take-out double over pre-empts.

20. All four players have equal responsibility.

Chapter 2

Hearts Hearts Hearts

We run through the set of hearts in this chapter – one to seven and then a few more to boot. See whether it is your favourite suit. The chapter finishes with a smaller trivia section dealing with laws and ethics in common situations.

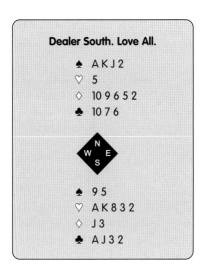

Dealer South. Love All.

♠ A K J 2
♡ 5
◇ 10 9 6 5 2
♣ 10 7 6

♠ 9 5
♡ A K 8 3 2
◇ J 3
♣ A J 3 2

South	West	North	East
1♡	Double	All Pass	

West leads the ◇A (East playing the ◇8), followed by the ♡4 to East's ♡9.

Five top tricks. What is the best line to seven tricks?

A

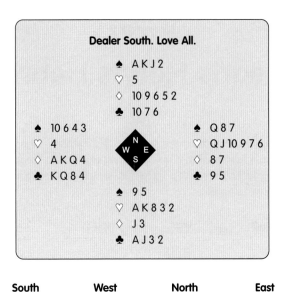

Dealer South. Love All.

```
            ♠ A K J 2
            ♡ 5
            ◇ 10 9 6 5 2
            ♣ 10 7 6
♠ 10 6 4 3                  ♠ Q 8 7
♡ 4                         ♡ Q J 10 9 7 6
◇ A K Q 4      N            ◇ 8 7
♣ K Q 8 4    W   E          ♣ 9 5
                 S
            ♠ 9 5
            ♡ A K 8 3 2
            ◇ J 3
            ♣ A J 3 2
```

South	West	North	East
1♡	Double	All Pass	

West leads the ◇A (East playing the ◇8), followed by the ♡4 to East's ♡9.

The first thing to realise is that East needs extreme trump length and strength to pass a one-level take-out double, so we can place him with all the remaining high trumps.

There are various possibilities for extra tricks; the spade finesse and a ruff would bring us up to seven, but what is the safest way?

Little harm can be done by exiting straightaway with a second diamond. East appears to have a doubleton (otherwise West might have continued the suit). West wins and exits with a spade which we win with ace. We now lead a diamond through East.

If he ruffs high, we throw a club and when he continues with, say, the queen of hearts, we duck. Then he switches to a club, which we win, play a spade to the king, ruff a spade, and exit with a club – we will make the last two tricks with ♡K8 sitting over ♡J7.

If East discards on the third diamond (a spade) we ruff small, cash the king of spades and lead another diamond. East must ruff high (or we have seven tricks), but we are now left with ♡K83 over ♡QJ76 and must make two trumps (ducking the first lead of an honour). With the ace of clubs too, we make seven tricks.

No need to rely on the spade finesse after all.

Q

Dealer East. Love All.

```
          ♠ 10 7 5
          ♡ Q 10 8 4 2
          ◇ 9 4
          ♣ Q J 9
♠ 9 3
♡ J 3
◇ J 10 7 5 2        N
♣ A 6 5 2       W   E
                    S
```

South	West	North	East
			1♠
1NT	Pass	2◇¹	Pass
2♡	All Pass		

¹transfer to hearts, which South obeys

West leads the ♠9; partner takes the ♠K followed by the ♠A and then continues with the ♠6 (the middle of his three remaining cards), which we ruff.

A good start to the defence, but what next?

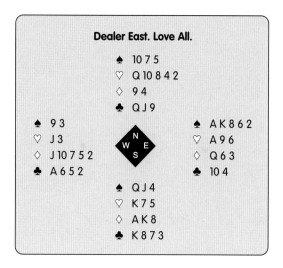

Dealer East. Love All.

	♠ 10 7 5	
	♡ Q 10 8 4 2	
	◇ 9 4	
	♣ Q J 9	

♠ 9 3		♠ A K 8 6 2
♡ J 3		♡ A 9 6
◇ J 10 7 5 2		◇ Q 6 3
♣ A 6 5 2		♣ 10 4

	♠ Q J 4	
	♡ K 7 5	
	◇ A K 8	
	♣ K 8 7 3	

South	West	North	East
			1♠
1NT	Pass	2◇¹	Pass
2♡	All Pass		

¹transfer to hearts, which South obeys

West leads the ♠9; partner takes the ♠K followed by the ♠A and then continues with the ♠6 (the middle of his three remaining cards), which we ruff.

The defence starts well, but the middle spade suggests a lack of useful high cards in the minor suits. With no quick entry to partner's hand, there is no prospect of a trump promotion.

So we have the first three tricks, but where are our next three tricks coming from? Ace of clubs, a trump trick and …? There does not seem to be a diamond loser; with the ace, partner would have signalled for a diamond (returned his highest spade) and with the king, the finesse is right for declarer. Clubs don't look very hopeful either! But maybe there is a chance – if partner has a doubleton club we should be able to give him a ruff.

Underlead the ace of clubs. Now if partner has king doubleton we can give him a ruff immediately; if not, as in this hand, partner may have the ace of trumps. In this case, declarer wins the club switch and plays a trump, but partner takes his ace and returns a second club for us to win and return a club for a ruff and the setting trick.

Q

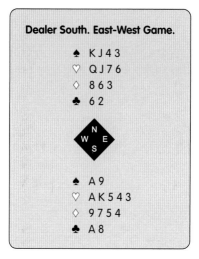

Dealer South. East-West Game.

    ♠ K J 4 3
    ♡ Q J 7 6
    ◇ 8 6 3
    ♣ 6 2

    ♠ A 9
    ♡ A K 5 4 3
    ◇ 9 7 5 4
    ♣ A 8

South	West	North	East
1♡¹	Pass	2♡	Pass
3◇	Pass	3♡	All Pass

¹four-card majors

West leads the ◇K, overtaken by East's ace, followed by a diamond to West's ◇10; West follows with the ◇Q (East throwing a club) and ◇J.

North-South have stopped short of game, which would have been a reasonable proposition. South took a conservative view of his hand – with the extra heart, he is probably worth a game bid after his partner's simple raise. Playing four-card majors North is quite correct in turning down the game try because his diamond holding is as bad as it could be.

It is particularly important to make sure that we make 3♡.

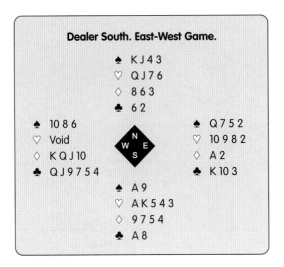

Dealer South. East-West Game.

	♠ K J 4 3	
	♡ Q J 7 6	
	◇ 8 6 3	
	♣ 6 2	

♠ 10 8 6		♠ Q 7 5 2
♡ Void	N	♡ 10 9 8 2
◇ K Q J 10	W E	◇ A 2
♣ Q J 9 7 5 4	S	♣ K 10 3

	♠ A 9	
	♡ A K 5 4 3	
	◇ 9 7 5 4	
	♣ A 8	

South	West	North	East
1♡¹	Pass	2♡	Pass
3◇	Pass	3♡	All Pass

¹four-card majors

West leads the ◇K, overtaken by East's ace, followed by a diamond to
West's ◇10; West follows with the ◇Q (East throwing a club) and ◇J.

At the table, declarer, angry at having missed game, ruffed high (East
throwing a second club) and played a heart to the king. He drew three
rounds of trumps, took a spade finesse and went one down. His anger at the
bidding now looked rather silly.

Whenever we are disappointed at missing our best contract, we should
try extra hard to make the one we are in. It might be the day when every
suit breaks badly!

After ruffing with the queen of hearts, declarer should have played a
club to the ace and cashed the ace of hearts. There were now two lines of
play available: the spade finesse or a dummy reversal. The latter is by far
the better option especially given East's club discards.

Declarer should continue with the ace-king of spades and a spade ruff,
then a heart to the jack, and another spade. If East has to follow, declarer
is home (three ruffs, three top trumps and three top tricks), but even if he
can ruff, declarer can simply discard a club and take the last two tricks with
the ♡K5.

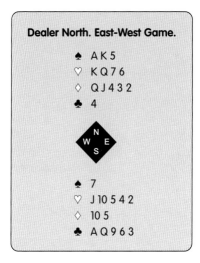

Dealer North. East-West Game.

♠ A K 5
♡ K Q 7 6
◇ Q J 4 3 2
♣ 4

♠ 7
♡ J 10 5 4 2
◇ 10 5
♣ A Q 9 6 3

South	West	North	East
		1◇	Pass
1♡	Pass	4♣¹	Pass
4♡	All Pass		

¹splinter bid, showing shortage in clubs as well as heart support

West leads the ◇6 to East's king; the ◇A follows,
West discarding a spade, and then East plays a third diamond.

North valued his hand as a raise to 4♡ and so showed his shortage on the way. It is certainly borderline for a raise to game, but here it has turned out well enough. South has no great ambition and so simply converts back to game.

This good game looks rather more precarious after the opening two tricks. How can we avoid a fourth loser?

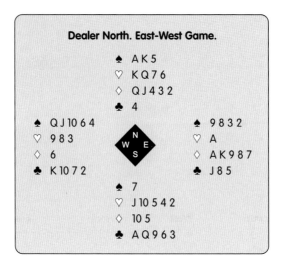

Dealer North. East-West Game.

	♠ A K 5	
	♡ K Q 7 6	
	◇ Q J 4 3 2	
	♣ 4	
♠ Q J 10 6 4		♠ 9 8 3 2
♡ 9 8 3		♡ A
◇ 6		◇ A K 9 8 7
♣ K 10 7 2		♣ J 8 5
	♠ 7	
	♡ J 10 5 4 2	
	◇ 10 5	
	♣ A Q 9 6 3	

South	West	North	East
		1◇	Pass
1♡	Pass	4♣¹	Pass
4♡	All Pass		

¹splinter bid, showing shortage in clubs as well as heart support

West leads the ◇6 to East's king; the ◇A follows,
West discarding a spade, and then East plays a third diamond.

Clearly we cannot afford an overruff (except by the ace), so we should ruff high (West discarding another spade). If we simply play a heart from hand to the king East may win the ace and another diamond will force us to ruff high again, promoting a trick for West's ♡98.

So we cross to the ace of spades and lead a trump from table. Now when East plays the ace, we can ruff the fourth diamond high without cost (West discards another spade). We cross to the king of hearts and East shows out. We have nine tricks (two spades, three hearts in dummy, two ruffs in hand, a diamond and a club) and need one more. We have a choice of plays: to ruff a spade in hand or to finesse in clubs?

West is likely to have started with five spades otherwise East would have held five as well as his red suit honours and surely a 1♠ overcall would have been tempting. So the danger of an overruff, even after West has discarded three spades, is minimal. Thus we ruff a spade in hand, cash the ace of clubs and ruff a club to return to dummy to draw trumps and claim.

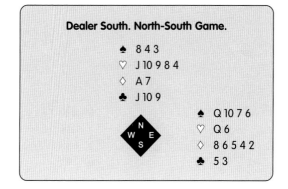

Dealer South. North-South Game.

```
              ♠ 8 4 3
              ♡ J 10 9 8 4
              ◇ A 7
              ♣ J 10 9
                              ♠ Q 10 7 6
                              ♡ Q 6
                 N            ◇ 8 6 5 4 2
              W     E         ♣ 5 3
                 S
```

South	West	North	East
1♡	Double	4♡	4♠
5♡	All Pass		

West leads the ◇Q, which runs to declarer's king;
he cashes the ♡A and ♡K on which partner discards the ♣8 and ♣2.

4♠ was quite a bid on East's pile of rubbish, but at the vulnerability, it might well have been a good save. Can we make things even better by taking 5♡ off?

What is there to think about?

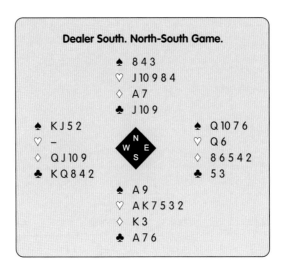

Dealer South. North-South Game.

	♠ 8 4 3	
	♡ J 10 9 8 4	
	◇ A 7	
	♣ J 10 9	

♠ K J 5 2		♠ Q 10 7 6
♡ –		♡ Q 6
◇ Q J 10 9		◇ 8 6 5 4 2
♣ K Q 8 4 2		♣ 5 3

	♠ A 9	
	♡ A K 7 5 3 2	
	◇ K 3	
	♣ A 7 6	

South	West	North	East
1♡	Double	4♡	4♠
5♡	All Pass		

West leads the ◇Q, which runs to declarer's king;
he cashes the ♡A and ♡K on which partner discards the ♣8 and ♣2.

At the table, declarer continued with a diamond to the ace and a small spade to the six, nine and partner's jack. West continued with a spade which declarer won. Now he crossed to dummy in trumps and ruffed a spade, crossed to dummy once again in trumps and led the jack of clubs which ran to West's king. Poor West was left with three nasty options: a spade or diamond would give declarer a ruff and discard, and a club would give declarer the last two tricks in that suit – 5♡ made.

More careful defence requires East to save his partner from such an awful end, by making sure it is he who wins the defence's spade trick. When declarer leads a spade we should insert the ten, forcing him to win and try the nine of spades, but partner lets this run to our queen and we can now lead a club which breaks up declarer's endplay. He has to let West win the club, but West can safely exit with a spade. Now declarer has lost two tricks and cannot afford another loser – his only chance is the second club finesse, but of course, our heroic partner can win the setting trick.

Dealer East. North-South Game.
Teams of Four.

```
        ♠ 9 8 3
        ♡ A K 5 4
        ◇ A K 4 2
        ♣ A 9

              N
          W       E
              S

        ♠ Void
        ♡ Q 7 6 3
        ◇ 10 9 8 7 3
        ♣ K 4 3 2
```

South	West	North	East
	2♠¹	Double	4♠
5♡	Pass	6♡	All Pass

¹a weak two

West leads the ♠K.

South was very bold to bid 5♡! And North did not hesitate in going for slam. 6◇ is the best spot, making against most breaks, but we still have reasonable chances where we are.

It is unlikely we can cope with a 4-1 break in trumps, but how about a 3-1 break in diamonds?

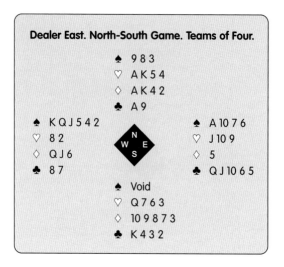

Dealer East. North-South Game. Teams of Four.

```
                ♠ 9 8 3
                ♡ A K 5 4
                ◇ A K 4 2
                ♣ A 9
  ♠ K Q J 5 4 2              ♠ A 10 7 6
  ♡ 8 2          N           ♡ J 10 9
  ◇ Q J 6      W   E         ◇ 5
  ♣ 8 7          S           ♣ Q J 10 6 5
                ♠ Void
                ♡ Q 7 6 3
                ◇ 10 9 8 7 3
                ♣ K 4 3 2
```

South	West	North	East
	2♠¹	Double	4♠
5♡	Pass	6♡	All Pass

¹a weak two

West leads the ♠K.

How many spade ruffs do we need? Well, if we make four diamonds, two clubs and four hearts, then we need two spade ruffs. But if we take two ruffs and draw trumps and diamonds break 3-1, the defence will win their diamond and cash a spade. We could try for three ruffs – ruff the lead, ace of diamonds, spade ruff, ace of clubs, spade ruff, cash the queen of hearts, but how do we get back to dummy? A diamond is best but loses to many likely distributions.

There is a better line than this which is to combine the lines described above. To do this, we aim to lose our diamond trick before drawing trumps. Ruff the lead and run the ten of diamonds!

If West covers, ruff a spade and then play the nine of diamonds, running it if West plays small. This line loses only when West has a small singleton diamond and even so, the defence must be very alert as it will not be obvious to East that he can give his partner a ruff.

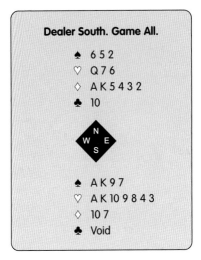

Dealer South. Game All.

```
              ♠ 6 5 2
              ♡ Q 7 6
              ◇ A K 5 4 3 2
              ♣ 10

                 N
              W     E
                 S

              ♠ A K 9 7
              ♡ A K 10 9 8 4 3
              ◇ 10 7
              ♣ Void
```

South	West	North	East
2♡	Pass	4◇¹	Pass
4♠	Pass	5◇	Pass
7♡	All Pass		

¹a good diamond suit and support for hearts

West leads the ♣5; you ruff and play the ♡A but East shows out.

North's diamond bids were ideal for South. After the second bid, he could feel sure that, with North holding three hearts, 7♡ would be a good prospect.

A reasonable grand slam if trumps break 2-1, but unfortunately things are starting to look bad.

Can we still make?

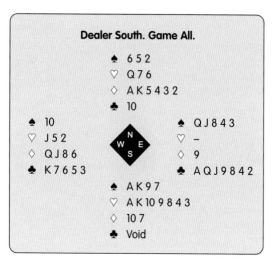

Dealer South. Game All.

	North		
	♠ 6 5 2		
	♡ Q 7 6		
	◇ A K 5 4 3 2		
	♣ 10		

West		East
♠ 10		♠ Q J 8 4 3
♡ J 5 2		♡ –
◇ Q J 8 6		◇ 9
♣ K 7 6 5 3		♣ A Q J 9 8 4 2

	South		
	♠ A K 9 7		
	♡ A K 10 9 8 4 3		
	◇ 10 7		
	♣ Void		

South	West	North	East
2♡	Pass	4◇[1]	Pass
4♠	Pass	5◇	Pass
7♡	All Pass		

[1] a good diamond suit and support for hearts

West leads the ♣5; you ruff and play the ♡A but East shows out.

Which trump did you use to ruff the club? Not the three or four? Good, then you can still make 7♡.

We need to establish diamonds before drawing trumps because our only entry (after the suit is established) is in trumps. We need West to have at least a doubleton diamond. To test this, after the first round of trumps we try the ace and king of diamonds and are surprised to discover that West holds four, leaving East with a very extreme distribution. Ruff the third diamond with the nine and lead the three of hearts; West puts in the jack and we win the queen. A second diamond ruffed with the ten establishes the suit and finally we lead our carefully preserved four of hearts to dummy's seven and can cash our two diamond winners for two spade discards – thirteen tricks.

If you ruffed the first trick with the three or four, you have no way back. As shown, if you lead the small trump, West will play the jack and if you play the ten, West will duck, leaving you with only one entry to dummy.

You are playing standard leads against no-trump contracts – fourth highest from an honour, second highest from a bad suit, top of an honour sequence, etc – what would you play on your partner's lead in the following situations? There is no particular urgency to switch; your aim is to secure as many heart tricks as possible.

(1)

Lead: ♡4

Dummy plays ♡7

(2)

Lead: ♡8

Dummy plays ♡6

(3)

Lead: ♡10

Dummy plays ♡2

(4)

Lead: ♡K

Dummy plays ♡6

(5)

Lead: ♡8

Dummy plays ♡5

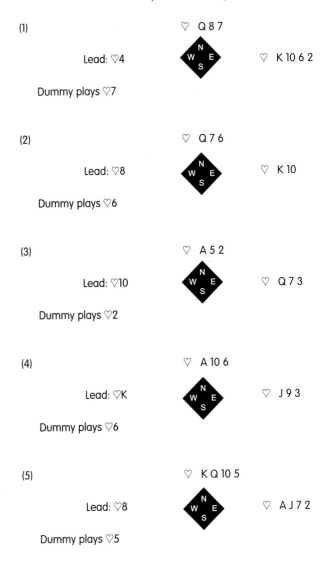

(1) ♡ Q 8 7 — ♡ K 10 6 2

(2) ♡ Q 7 6 — ♡ K 10

(3) ♡ A 5 2 — ♡ Q 7 3

(4) ♡ A 10 6 — ♡ J 9 3

(5) ♡ K Q 10 5 — ♡ A J 7 2

A **(1)**   ♡ Q 8 7

♡ J 9 5 4   ♡ K 10 6 2

♡ A 3

Play the ten. Playing the king never gains – it always yields a trick to the queen. It might appear that, when partner has led from the ace (without the jack) we give a trick away, but we must always lose a trick in the suit, so it matters little that we give this trick up on the first round rather than on a later one.

(2)   ♡ Q 7 6

♡ A J 9 8 2   ♡ K 10

♡ 5 4 3

Play the ten. Again, playing the king always yields a trick to the queen.

(3)   ♡ A 5 2

♡ K 10 9 6 4   ♡ Q 7 3

♡ J 8

Play the queen. The ten denies the jack, and so the play of the queen cannot lose. The important instance is as above, when our partner has led from an interior sequence.

(4)   ♡ A 10 6

♡ K Q 8 7 2   ♡ J 9 3

♡ 5 4

Play the nine. One look at dummy's holding in hearts persuades us not to unblock the jack, but we do want partner to continue the suit, so the best card is the nine.

(5)   ♡ K Q 10 5

♡ 9 8 6 3   ♡ A J 7 2

♡ 4

Play the two. Here declarer has been clever; guessing that the lead is from a bad suit, he played low from dummy to pretend he held the nine. If he had played a higher heart he was booked for three losers. Had we played the jack he would have made two tricks in the suit. If declarer does have the nine he still makes only two tricks when we play low.

Many people now play an overcall in the opener's suit as a Michaels cue-bid, showing a two-suited hand: it is very similar to the Unusual 2NT, which anchors around the minor suits.

The Michaels cue-bid anchors around the major suits: when the opened suit is a minor, eg 1◊, then an overcall of 2◊ is the Michaels cue-bid and shows 5-5 in the major suits. If the opening was a major, then the Michaels cue-bid shows the other major and one of the minors. The bid is made on weak hands or on very strong hands – most of the strength tends to be within the two long suits.

Let us see how you do with these four problems which all involve a lot of hearts. The Michaels cue-bid is asterisked in each case.

(1) Dealer South. Love All.

♠ K 5
♡ A Q 5 4 3
◊ A Q 5 4
♣ 7 2

South	West	North	East
Pass	1♡	2♡*	3♡
Pass	?		

(2) Dealer South. Love All.

♠ A 5
♡ 6
◊ Q 9 6 3 2
♣ J 10 9 5 2

South	West	North	East
1♡	2♡*	4♡	?

(3) Dealer South. Love All.

♠ A 3 2
♡ K J 7 6
◊ K 8 3 2
♣ 6 4

South	West	North	East
Pass	1♡	2♡*	?

(4) Dealer South. Love All.

♠ A 7 6 4 2
♡ 7
◊ K Q 10 5 3
♣ Q 3

South	West	North	East
1♡	2♡*	3♡	?

In competitive auctions it is important to differentiate between hands that simply have support for partner and hands that also have strength. Direct raises of a suit are used to show the weaker hands and a cue-bid (a bid of the opponent's suit) to show stronger hands.

(1)

♠ K 5	♠ 6 3
♡ A Q 5 4 3	♡ K 9 7 6
◇ A Q 5 4	◇ K 7 2
♣ 7 2	♣ J 9 5 4

Pass – We have a good hand, but if partner had wanted to invite to game he would have bid 2♠ (see above).

(2)

♠ K 9 7 6 3	♠ A 5
♡ 4 2	♡ 6
◇ K J 10 8 5	◇ Q 9 6 3 2
♣ 3	♣ J 10 9 5 2

4NT – We have only one defensive trick and a known ten card fit in a minor. It seems likely that 4♡ will make and that we will have a good sacrifice in a minor. 4NT asks partner to bid his minor.

(3)

♠ K 5	♠ A 3 2
♡ A Q 5 4 3	♡ K J 7 6
◇ A Q 5 4	◇ K 8 3 2
♣ 7 2	♣ 6 4

Direct raises show competitive hands as mentioned above and seen in (1) (the same West hand is used in both). Here we have a genuine raise to 3♡ so we use a bid of the opponent's suit: 2♠ – it shows support for hearts and at least the strength for a raise to 3♡ (it can be much stronger).

(4)

♠ K Q 10 5 3	♠ A 7 6 4 2
♡ 10 4	♡ 7
◇ A J 7 6 2	◇ K Q 10 5 3
♣ 4	♣ Q 3

4◇ – Any new suit at such a level tends to promise support for partner, especially after two-suited overcalls. By bidding 4◇ here we tell partner two things: we want to bid 4♠ and most of our values outside the trump suit lie in diamonds. Knowing this partner can bid 5♠ over 5♡, crucial on this deal as both sides can make five-level contracts.

Below are some bidding problems of a different nature. Do you know how to resolve these common mistakes?

(1)	South	West	North	East
	1♡	2♡¹	2♡	?

¹Michaels Cue Bid showing spades and a minor

You are sitting East and hear this rather strange auction. North does not correct his bid in the same breath, but he clearly intended to bid 3♡. What is the position?

(2)	South	West	North	East
	1♡	?	2♡	Pass

Sitting West, your right-hand opponent deals and opens 1♡ and your left-hand opponent raises to 2♡ followed by a pass from partner. You did not get a chance to bid. What redress do you have?

(3)	South	West	North	East
		Pass (1♡)	Double	?

This can be rather a common auction in a noisy rubber bridge club. A Pass can too easily sound like 1♡ and here, that is exactly what North thought and thus doubled, but West quickly mentioned that he had nothing to double. What is the position?

(4)	♠ 5 2		South	West	North	East
	♡ K Q 4 3 2		1NT¹	Pass	2♡²	Pass
	◇ 6 3 2		3♡	Pass	?	
	♣ 5 4 2		¹strong no-trump (15–17)			
			²partner alerts your bid			
			as a transfer to spades			

Your partner is so used to playing Duplicate Bridge that he has forgotten that you do not play transfers at Rubber Bridge. So he alerts 2♡ as a transfer and bids 3♡ which shows good support for spades (!) and a feature in hearts. What do you do? Are you allowed to pass?

(1) There are two options neither of which incur any penalty for the North-South side. Either you accept the bid of 2♡ and continue as normal, or you ask South to correct his bid, and by correcting it to 3♡ (same suit, lowest level) there is no penalty and once again the bidding continues as usual.

(2) None, because your partner has condoned North's 'bid out of turn', and so the bidding continues as normal. In most cases like this, including insufficient bids in (1) above, if the next player makes a bid he condones the previous call and the auction continues without penalty or effect. The case when this cannot occur is in (3) below when the call is illegal.

(3) North has made an illegal bid. This *must* be cancelled and the offender (North) must substitute a legal bid, but there is a penalty which requires his partner (South) to pass throughout the auction.
   This is Law 36, but of course at Rubber Bridge, with no director, the use and carrying out of the laws is up to the players' own discretion. Here, where there was clearly a misheard bid, and with such noise around, it would seem more sensible to redeal the hand or restart the auction. But this leniency can only be shown if both players of the non-offending side agree.

(4) Of course, you are allowed to pass. You have to respond as if partner had never said anything and thus 3♡ is an esoteric raise of a weak take-out! Whatever hand partner holds, you are certainly not worth anything but pass. It is your partner who is doing strange things and you can just be thankful that he chose to bid 3♡ rather than anything else! The opponents do have the right of redress if they feel they have been damaged (for example if one of them was going to bid spades the alert might well affect the outcome of the hand).
   Having passed 3♡, when you become declarer it is important that you inform the defenders of the misinformation before they lead.
   As to whether anyone is damaged, it is up to the four players to judge, although it is helpful to have a non-playing arbiter such as a suitably qualified spectator, or a player at another table.

Chapter 3

Duplicate Pairs

Duplicate bridge, where every pair plays the same hands, is a variation which aims to reduce the 'luck of the cards'. In this game, every point counts, which makes no-trumps the most desirable contract and makes overtricks invaluable. A precious overtrick (or undertrick) can be worth as much as a grand slam. Many more conventions are used in this form of bridge and the bidding tends to be more competitive than in Rubber.

Dealer South. Game All. Duplicate Pairs.

♠ 5 3
♡ A Q 10 8
◇ 8 4
♣ Q 9 7 6 2

South	West	North	East
1◇	Pass	2◇[1]	Pass
2♠	Pass	3♣[2]	Pass
3◇	Pass	3♠	Pass
4♠	All Pass		

[1] inverted minor raise, ten or more points with four or more diamonds
[2] no-trump probe, showing values in clubs

At Duplicate, the last thing anybody tries is a minor-suit game. Here it looks as though our opponents are trying a 4-3 spade fit to try to grab those extra few points. How are we going to foil their plan?

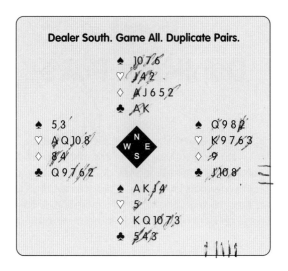

Dealer South. Game All. Duplicate Pairs.

```
              ♠ 10 7 6
              ♡ J 4 2
              ◇ A J 6 5 2
              ♣ A K

  ♠ 5 3                        ♠ Q 9 8 2
  ♡ A Q 10 8         N         ♡ K 9 7 6 3
  ◇ 8 4          W       E     ◇ 9
  ♣ Q 9 7 6 2        S         ♣ J 10 8

              ♠ A K J 4
              ♡ 5
              ◇ K Q 10 7 3
              ♣ 5 4 3
```

South	West	North	East
1◇	Pass	2◇[1]	Pass
2♠	Pass	3♣[2]	Pass
3◇	Pass	3♠	Pass
4♠	All Pass		

[1] inverted minor raise, ten or more points with four or more diamonds
[2] no-trump probe, showing values in clubs

Our first thoughts are to lead trumps in order to restrict the ruffing power (especially of the short hand), but this is a mistake, given that North-South have a good source of tricks in diamonds.

The evidence seems to be in favour of attacking declarer's weakness rather than his trumps. We might not have an inviting holding in hearts, but if either North or South had held the king of hearts, they would surely have bid no-trumps, so it is a pretty safe lead.

We lead the ace of hearts and are happy to see that dummy holds three hearts, so we continue with a second heart which South ruffs, but now he has lost control – East has the most trumps.

There is actually nothing declarer can do. He might try drawing two rounds of trumps (by way of a finesse) and then play on diamonds, but when East ruffs in he plays another heart and declarer must go one down.

As you can see, North-South's greed was wrongly directed for they can actually make 6◇. It does not always pay to shun a minor-suit fit.

Bernard Magee's Bridge Quiz Book

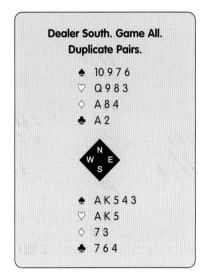

Dealer South. Game All.
Duplicate Pairs.

♠ 10 9 7 6
♡ Q 9 8 3
♢ A 8 4
♣ A 2

♠ A K 5 4 3
♡ A K 5
♢ 7 3
♣ 7 6 4

South	West	North	East
1♠	Pass	3♠	Pass
4♠	All Pass		

West leads the ♣K ducked, followed by the ♣Q.

A simple auction for once! The contract looks to be pretty safe, but this is Pairs remember, and we are trying to score as many overtricks as possible.

We duck the lead, win the continuation and then play a trump to the ace, West dropping the jack. What next?

Once we have sorted out the trump suit we will switch our attention to the hearts. The ace and king of hearts bring the ten from East on the second round. Another guess or ...?

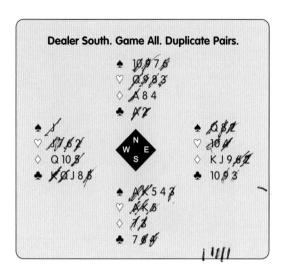

Dealer South. Game All. Duplicate Pairs.

South	West	North	East
1♠	Pass	3♠	Pass
4♠	All Pass		

West leads the ♣K ducked, followed by the ♣Q.

The problems faced in this hand involve the Principle of Restricted Choice. Applying this to the trump suit – it states that, since West was equally likely to play jack or queen from queen jack doubleton, the probability of his having that holding is diminished (approximately halved) by virtue of his playing the jack. Thus the odds are in favour of playing West to have started with jack singleton.

So we cross to dummy with a club ruff and lead the ten of spades, playing low when East refuses to cover. The king finishes the job of drawing trumps.

Now the hearts. The principle applies similarly here – if East held ♡J104 he was equally likely to play the ten or jack on the second round and so, adjusting the odds accordingly, we also finesse in hearts and pick up that suit for no loser too, discarding a diamond on the fourth heart to secure twelve tricks.

Q

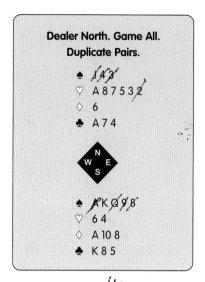

Dealer North. Game All.
Duplicate Pairs.

♠ J 4 3
♡ A 8 7 5 3 2
◇ 6
♣ A 7 4

```
      N
   W     E
      S
```

♠ A K Q 9 8
♡ 6 4
◇ A 10 8
♣ K 8 5

South	West	North	East
		Pass	Pass
1♠	Pass	2♡	Pass
2NT	Pass	3♠	Pass
4♠	All Pass		

West leads the ♠7.

North-South were playing Acol with a weak no-trump, so South's 2NT rebid promised at least four spades and 15–16 points, but North was happy to push to game, suggesting spades rather than no-trumps and South quickly assented.

Remember, this is Pairs: with the contract looking safe, what about those precious overtricks?

A

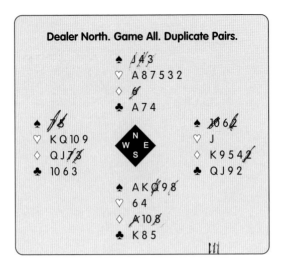

Dealer North. Game All. Duplicate Pairs.

```
              ♠ J A 3
              ♡ A 8 7 5 3 2
              ◊ 9
              ♣ A 7 4
    ♠ 7 5                    ♠ 10 6 4
    ♡ K Q 10 9       N       ♡ J
    ◊ Q J 7 3     W     E    ◊ K 9 5 4 2
    ♣ 10 6 3         S       ♣ Q J 9 2
              ♠ A K Q 9 8
              ♡ 6 4
              ◊ A 10 8
              ♣ K 8 5
```

South	West	North	East
		Pass	Pass
1♠	Pass	2♡	Pass
2NT	Pass	3♠	Pass
4♠	All Pass		

West leads the ♠7.

At the table, South won the trump on table, played a diamond to the ace and ruffed a diamond, a club to the king and ruffed another diamond. Then the ace of hearts and another heart. He eventually made eleven tricks, losing just a heart and a club. Pleased with himself, he looked at the traveller as North scored the board only to discover he had a below average score.

With plenty of time to establish winners, he should have played on the heart suit rather than take ruffs in dummy. Win the trump lead in hand and play ace and another heart. Now, win the trump return in dummy and ruff a heart, cash the ace of diamonds and ruff a diamond, then ruff one more heart, establishing the suit and draw trumps. Finally a club to dummy allows us to enjoy the heart suit – five spades, one ruff, three hearts, two aces and one king adds up to twelve tricks.

Notice that we managed twelve tricks with a 4-1 heart split. Similarly we can cope with most 4-1 trump breaks if hearts are 3-2 and will usually make at least eleven tricks by this method in any event.

Q The bidding is more aggressive in Duplicate Pairs than in other forms of bridge. The partscore battles are much more fierce because the difference between –100 and –110 is so large (whilst, in Teams or Rubber, it is so little). Thus 2♠–2, non-vulnerable (–100) is better than allowing the opposition to make 2♡ (–110). But if the opposition are aggressive too, they will double the tight contracts and turn +100 into +300. As you can see, there is a fine line between success and failure! Let us see how aggressive you are:

(1) Dealer West. Love All.

	♠ 7 6	South	West	North	East
	♡ K Q J 3 2		1◇	Pass	2◇
	◇ 6 5	?			
	♣ Q 10 3 2				

(2) Dealer West. East-West Game.

	♠ K Q 7 4	South	West	North	East
	♡ A 6		1◇	Pass	1♡
	◇ 10 7 5 4	Pass	2♣	Pass	Pass
	♣ 8 7 6	?			

(3) Dealer South. Love All.

	♠ A Q 5 4 3	South	West	North	East
	♡ Q 10 3 2	1♠	2♣	Pass	Pass
	◇ Q J 10 7	?			
	♣ Void				

(4) Dealer East. Love All.

	♠ A 10 9 6	South	West	North	East
	♡ K Q 5				1♠
	◇ Q 7 6	Pass	Pass	Double	Pass
	♣ Q J 3	?			

(5) Dealer South. Love All.

	♠ K 8 6	South	West	North	East
	♡ A Q J 3 2	1♡	Double	3♡	Pass
	◇ A K 5	?			
	♣ 7 4				

(1) 2♡ – We need to get into the auction. The bid is risky, but if West passes, partner may be left with a hand such as ♠K542 ♡874 ♢873 ♣AK9 and nothing to say. The positive sides to this type of bid far outweigh the negative.

(2) 2♠ – On the bidding, we are likely to have a seven- or eight-card fit. The point is that if partner has a mixed hand (eg ♠J853 ♡K952 ♢Q83 ♣A3), he will have been unable to enter the auction and so it is not unreasonable to harbour thoughts of making 2♠. Passing out 2♣ at Duplicate is unusual as East is likely to be pretty weak for his bidding. With the hand above, we will be able to make seven or eight tricks in spades whilst our opponents make eight or nine in clubs. These aggressive actions can go wrong, but more often than not they earn a good score.

(3) 2♢ – Do not be tempted to make a take-out double, because it is more than likely that partner is ready to pass with clubs sitting over West. Our hand is not fit for defence of a club contract. It is weak in points and controls and partner is likely to be rather annoyed as declarer racks up eight tricks in clubs. North may well hold: ♠86 ♡754 ♢K95 ♣AQ842. If we are lucky, we might make a diamond, three trumps and two spades but even that may not score well if we can make more than 100 in a partscore.

(4) 2NT – Do not punish partner for protecting. This hand looks worth a raise to 3NT, but think again. Partner may be bidding on a hand of less than opening strength in order to keep the bidding open for hands where we were unable to find a bid, such as this one. North may hold: ♠4 ♡AJ43 ♢A982 ♣10742. In response to a protective double, 1NT would show 9–11 points and 2NT 12–14.

(5) Pass – Remember that partner's bid is pre-emptive not invitational. He will have been stretching in order to make it more difficult for East to respond to his partner's double. His hand will be of the type that would have responded 2♡ normally, perhaps: ♠52 ♡K964 ♢J876 ♣Q62.

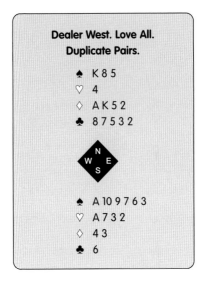

Dealer West. Love All.
Duplicate Pairs.

♠ K 8 5
♡ 4
♢ A K 5 2
♣ 8 7 5 3 2

♠ A 10 9 7 6 3
♡ A 7 3 2
♢ 4 3
♣ 6

South	West	North	East
	1♡	Double	3♡
4♠	All Pass		

West leads the ♣A followed by ♣K.

North must have viewed his hand with some trepidation as he placed it on the table, but South was happy enough. North's thin double had paid off and indeed South was not simply thinking of making the contract but searching for overtricks!

Can we make eleven tricks?

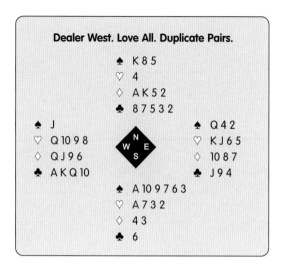

Dealer West. Love All. Duplicate Pairs.

♠ K 8 5
♡ 4
♢ A K 5 2
♣ 8 7 5 3 2

♠ J   ♠ Q 4 2
♡ Q 10 9 8   ♡ K J 6 5
♢ Q J 9 6   ♢ 10 8 7
♣ A K Q 10   ♣ J 9 4

♠ A 10 9 7 6 3
♡ A 7 3 2
♢ 4 3
♣ 6

South	West	North	East
	1♡	Double	3♡
4♠	All Pass		

West leads the ♣A followed by ♣K.

Making twelve tricks is impossible for it would involve ruffing with all dummy's trumps and so we would have to lose at least one trump to the ♠QJ (and the club at trick one). So we aim for eleven tricks – two heart ruffs, six trumps, ace of hearts, ace and king of diamonds.

Ruff the king of clubs and play a trump to the king (drawing West's jack) and then the ace of hearts followed by a heart ruff, a club ruff and a second heart ruff. By the Principle of Restricted Choice, we place East with two trumps left (♠Q4) so rather than cashing the ace of spades we continue: ace of diamonds, king of diamonds and ruff a diamond. And we can now exit with our losing heart to pick up the last two tricks with ♠A10 lying over East's holding. If no honour falls on the first round of trumps, we would do best to cash the ace of spades in the endgame.

It is interesting to note that North-South could have got their best score by defending 3♡ doubled, but only if North were to guess that a club lead was required in order for South to get three ruffs as well as the partnership's four top tricks, which would have resulted in three down and +500 (against the +450 for 4♠+1).

Dealer North. North-South Game. Duplicate Pairs.

```
                    ♠  K 6
                    ♡  A Q 9
                    ◇  A Q J 10 9 2
                    ♣  10 4
                                  ♠  10 8 5
                                  ♡  K 6 3 2
                N                 ◇  8 6 3
              W   E               ♣  K 8 7
                S
```

South	West	North	East
		1◇	Pass
2♣	Pass	3◇	Pass
3NT	All Pass		

West leads the ♠4 to dummy's ♠6, your ♠10 and declarer's ♠A;
declarer plays a heart to the ♡Q and your ♡K.

What next? Remember, this is Duplicate.

A

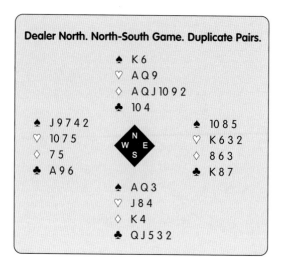

Dealer North. North-South Game. Duplicate Pairs.

	♠ K 6	
	♡ A Q 9	
	◊ A Q J 10 9 2	
	♣ 10 4	
♠ J 9 7 4 2		♠ 10 8 5
♡ 10 7 5		♡ K 6 3 2
◊ 7 5		◊ 8 6 3
♣ A 9 6		♣ K 8 7
	♠ A Q 3	
	♡ J 8 4	
	◊ K 4	
	♣ Q J 5 3 2	

South	West	North	East
		1◊	Pass
2♣	Pass	3◊	Pass
3NT	All Pass		

West leads the ♠4 to dummy's ♠6, your ♠10 and declarer's ♠A;
declarer plays a heart to the ♡Q and your ♡K.

Why has declarer not played diamonds? Probably because they are tricks in the bag, and with a likely two more from hearts and one more from spades, that is ten tricks. If South holds ♣AQ as well then he will be able to finesse for twelve tricks whatever we do. But there are a few situations where it does matter what we do, in particular where declarer holds the queen of spades. This card takes his trick tally up to eleven without any clubs at all.

Overtricks are all important in Duplicate so if we have tricks to cash we must do so before declarer gets back in. The only tricks we can have are in clubs, even though South has bid the suit. Which club should we lead? At first sight the king looks best but there is one more chance that we should not overlook. Declarer might hold just Qxxx or Jxxx in clubs. In both these cases, we *must* lead a small club so that partner can give us the lead on the second round of the suit to lead through declarer a second time.

Here the club switch pays rich dividends; we do not beat the contract but by holding declarer to ten tricks we should score very well.

Bernard Magee's Bridge Quiz Book

Q

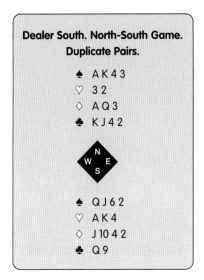

Dealer South. North-South Game.
Duplicate Pairs.

♠ A K 4 3
♡ 3 2
◇ A Q 3
♣ K J 4 2

♠ Q J 6 2
♡ A K 4
◇ J 10 4 2
♣ Q 9

South	West	North	East
1NT	2♣¹	2♡²	Pass
2NT	Pass	3NT	All Pass

¹hearts and another suit
²take-out of hearts

West leads the ♡Q.

South, so conscious of the importance of the extra ten points for no-trumps, thought that his double stop was the important feature to show rather than his four spades, hence he rebid 2NT, over which North settled for game (opposite a weak no-trump the maximum tally is 31 points and with no obvious eight-card fit…!). Thus we have arrived in the wrong contract. The majority of the field will be in 4♠ with an easy heart ruff and time to play on both minors. What can we do to beat them?

A

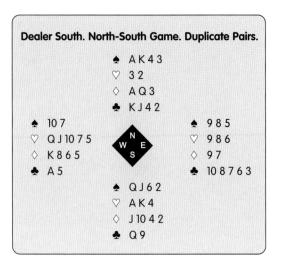

Dealer South. North-South Game. Duplicate Pairs.

```
                    ♠ A K 4 3
                    ♡ 3 2
                    ♢ A Q 3
                    ♣ K J 4 2
      ♠ 10 7                           ♠ 9 8 5
      ♡ Q J 10 7 5        N            ♡ 9 8 6
      ♢ K 8 6 5       W       E        ♢ 9 7
      ♣ A 5               S            ♣ 10 8 7 6 3
                    ♠ Q J 6 2
                    ♡ A K 4
                    ♢ J 10 4 2
                    ♣ Q 9
```

South	West	North	East
1NT	2♣¹	2♡²	Pass
2NT	Pass	3NT	All Pass

¹hearts and another suit
²take-out of hearts

West leads the ♡Q.

We win the lead and try spades – unfortunately they break! – so on the bidding, it seems most declarers will make twelve tricks (the diamond finesse is surely right) via four trumps, one ruff, two hearts, three diamonds and two clubs. In no-trumps, we can make three diamonds, four spades, two clubs and two hearts, a total of eleven tricks.

We need one more. If diamonds break 3-3 or if we pick up the doubleton king we can make one more there, but we cannot play for both those options so our chances are not high – less than 50% (especially with West having a four-card minor).

There is one less obvious chance, which is the club finesse. Yes, if East holds the ten of clubs, we can make three club tricks. This is 50% and our best hope. So win the ace of hearts, play the queen of spades, a spade to the ace and a club to the nine. West wins the ace of clubs and plays another heart. We win this, cash the queen of clubs and play the jack of diamonds covered by the king and ace – yes! – twelve tricks. From bottom to top ... not so fast, a few pairs had bid and made the 50% slam.

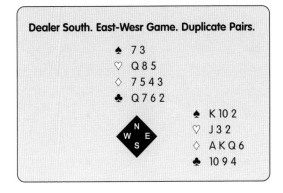

Dealer South. East-Wesr Game. Duplicate Pairs.

♠ 7 3
♡ Q 8 5
◊ 7 5 4 3
♣ Q 7 6 2

♠ K 10 2
♡ J 3 2
◊ A K Q 6
♣ 10 9 4

South	West	North	East
2NT	Pass	3NT	All Pass

West leads the ♡7 to the ♡8, ♡J and ♡A; then come the ♣A and ♣K
(♣5 and ♣3 from partner) and then the ◊J; we win the ◊Q
and cash the ◊A, partner discarding the ♡4.

South has shown 20–22 points in the auction, which leaves our partner
with 1–3 points! What is the best we can do, remembering that we are
playing Duplicate Bridge?

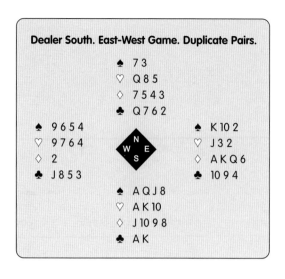

Dealer South. East-West Game. Duplicate Pairs.

```
                    ♠ 7 3
                    ♡ Q 8 5
                    ◇ 7 5 4 3
                    ♣ Q 7 6 2
     ♠ 9 6 5 4                        ♠ K 10 2
     ♡ 9 7 6 4          N             ♡ J 3 2
     ◇ 2            W       E         ◇ A K Q 6
     ♣ J 8 5 3          S             ♣ 10 9 4
                    ♠ A Q J 8
                    ♡ A K 10
                    ◇ J 10 9 8
                    ♣ A K
```

South	West	North	East
2NT	Pass	3NT	All Pass

West leads the ♡7 to the ♡8, ♡J and ♡A; then come the ♣A and ♣K
(♣5 and ♣3 from partner) and then the ◇J; we win the ◇Q
and cash the ◇A, partner discarding the ♡4.

The lead is doubtless 'second from nothing', but the four of hearts is a
significant discard for it suggests partner started with a four-card suit – he
discards the lowest from three remaining – which places declarer with
three.

It looks as though declarer's club play was in order to unblock, so
possibly partner has the jack of clubs; he also might have the queen of
spades. What is declarer's shape likely to be? Two clubs, three hearts, and
four diamonds; that leaves four spades, so he will have to play that suit
himself and there is no need to help him.

The best play is to continue with hearts. Declarer wins with the king
and plays a third round of diamonds. We win and once again return a heart.
On table for the only time with the queen of hearts, declarer cashes his
queen of clubs and tries the spade finesse. Now he cashes his winners in
hand, our king of spades winning the last trick. Nine tricks; a second spade
finesse would have brought the total to ten.

Remember, playing Duplicate, it is not necessarily our aim to take a
contract down, but to restrict Declarer to as few tricks as possible.

Bernard Magee's Bridge Quiz Book

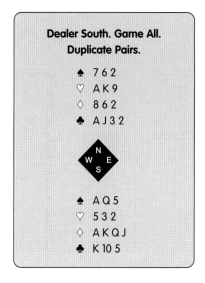

Dealer South. Game All.
Duplicate Pairs.

♠ 7 6 2
♡ A K 9
◇ 8 6 2
♣ A J 3 2

♠ A Q 5
♡ 5 3 2
◇ A K Q J
♣ K 10 5

South	West	North	East
2NT¹	Pass	4NT	All Pass

¹19–21 points

West leads the ♡Q.

A simple auction to a nice, safe contract. But remember, this is Pairs and making as many tricks as possible is the aim. Where do you start?

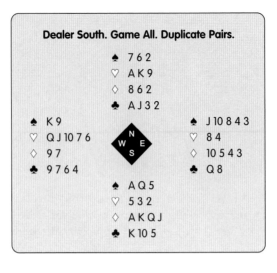

Dealer South. Game All. Duplicate Pairs.

```
                    ♠ 7 6 2
                    ♡ A K 9
                    ◇ 8 6 2
                    ♣ A J 3 2
     ♠ K 9                        ♠ J 10 8 4 3
     ♡ Q J 10 7 6        N        ♡ 8 4
     ◇ 9 7            W     E      ◇ 10 5 4 3
     ♣ 9 7 6 4           S        ♣ Q 8
                    ♠ A Q 5
                    ♡ 5 3 2
                    ◇ A K Q J
                    ♣ K 10 5
```

South	West	North	East
2NT¹	Pass	4NT	All Pass

¹19–21 points

West leads the ♡Q.

There is no point in ducking for we are not planning to give away the lead enough times to worry about the establishment of West's heart suit.

The club suit is the best place to start. Any hand holding four clubs to the queen will always take one trick, but if either hand has three to the queen we simply have to guess. If either defender has a doubleton queen it is better for us that it should be East for that will make the entry situation easier.

So the best line is to lead a club to the ten and cash the king dropping the queen. Now we cash four diamonds, throwing a spade and cash two more club tricks throwing a heart. That makes nine tricks and still two more top tricks to come. Now usually we would simply take the spade finesse, finishing with twelve tricks if successful or eleven tricks if not.

In this case, we notice that West discards two hearts on our minor-suit winners and it looks as if he is trying to hold on to his spades. We cash the king of hearts, drawing a heart from each defender and exit with our last heart. West wins this but his last two cards are both spades and he has to give us the last two tricks with the ♠AQ.

Q BRIDGE TRIVIA

1. What is a Howell?

2. What do you score for 2♣ redoubled +1, vulnerable in a Duplicate Pairs?

3. What is a Moysian fit?

4. Who or what is Meckwell?

5. It is Love All and you bid up to 6◇, expecting to make it, but your opponents bid 6♡ which your partner doubles and that ends the auction. How many tricks do you need to defeat 6♡ by to surpass the score you might have received for making 6◇?

6. Which is more likely, four cards, breaking 2-2, or six cards breaking 4-2?

7. What is an Arrow Switch?

8. At Duplicate Pairs, which player at each table is responsible for the proper observance of procedures of the game at that table?

9. What is Butler scoring?

10. What is a Curtain Card?

11. What are the only three successful contracts that can score 1000 points exactly, without overtricks, at Duplicate Bridge?

12. When would you use the term 'Stop' (or 'Skip') in bridge?

13. Which cards can be Minor Penalty Cards and which Major Penalty Cards?

14. To the winners of which competition is the Schwab Cup awarded?

15. What do the Rules of Eighteen and Nineteen relate to?

16. When might one defender ask his partner, 'Have you any questions?'?

17. What is a 'Rover'?

18. What is often called the 'Kiss of Death'?

19. What is the Law of Total Tricks?

20. There are three spades in dummy and declarer calls for a spade. Which one is deemed to have been called for?

A ANSWERS TO BRIDGE TRIVIA

1. It is a type of movement for Pairs play which when completed means that all pairs should have played each other once.

2. 1160.

3. A 4-3 trump fit.

4. The name given to the top American pair of Jeff MECKstroth and Eric RodWELL.

5. Five.

6. Six cards breaking 4-2; a 4-2 break = 48.4%, a 2-2 break = 40.7%.

7. The rotation of the boards through 90° so that East-West become North-South. It is used to obtain a single winning pair.

8. North.

9. It is a method for scoring Pairs events in IMPs. An average score, ignoring the highest and lowest scores is calculated for each board, the datum, and then scores are compared to that score as in Teams bridge.

10. A small piece of card for the recording of a hand in a duplicate board.

11. 3NT, 5♣ and 5♦ when redoubled and vulnerable.

12. In the auction, to preface a bid which skips a level (not usually done in Rubber Bridge).

13. Only non-honour cards can be minor penalty cards, but all cards may be major ones.

14. World Pairs Championship.

15. Opening bids. Rule of 18 for World Bridge Federation; Rule of 19 in England. It is the required sum of a player's two longest suits and high card points for a natural opening bid at the one level.

16. After placing his opening lead face down on the table.

17. A pair which displaces other pairs – in a duplicate with a half table, the rover pair ousts a different pair from their seats on each round.

18. A penalty of –200 on a partscore deal in a Pairs contest.

19. On any bridge hand, the total number of trumps (North-South's best fit + East-West's best fit) is approximately equal to the total number of tricks (the number of tricks North-South can make + the number East-West can make, in their respective contracts).

20. The smallest one.

Chapter 4

Doubles

Some of the more important contracts we play are often doubled – either because we are playing for money, or because one mistake might cost a big swing in a teams match. Whatever the situation the pressure is on. See how you fare. Then, of course, there is the 'double' dummy problem! The trivia section also continues the theme – more doubles!

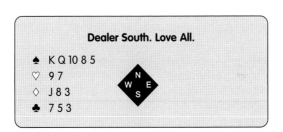

Dealer South. Love All.

♠ K Q 10 8 5
♡ 9 7
◇ J 8 3
♣ 7 5 3

South	West	North	East
1◇	Pass	1♡	Pass
1NT¹	Pass	3NT	Double
All Pass			

¹15–17 points

North-South were playing a weak no-trump, with the 1NT rebid showing a strong no-trump type of hand.

A freely bid 3NT and partner has doubled – what can that mean?

What should we lead?

A

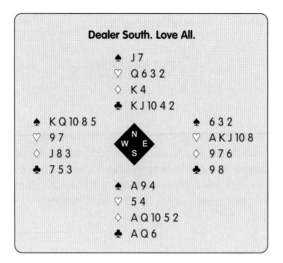

Dealer South. Love All.

```
                  ♠ J 7
                  ♡ Q 6 3 2
                  ◇ K 4
                  ♣ K J 10 4 2
   ♠ K Q 10 8 5              ♠ 6 3 2
   ♡ 9 7           N         ♡ A K J 10 8
   ◇ J 8 3      W     E      ◇ 9 7 6
   ♣ 7 5 3         S         ♣ 9 8
                  ♠ A 9 4
                  ♡ 5 4
                  ◇ A Q 10 5 2
                  ♣ A Q 6
```

South	West	North	East
1◇	Pass	1♡	Pass
1NT[1]	Pass	3NT	Double
All Pass			

[1]15–17 points

Partner has doubled a freely bid 3NT. This usually carries the message: 'Lead dummy's first (or only) bid suit.'

Can that be right now? We have such a good suit, surely …

Partner is in charge; he has made the double and surely has a good reason. He will take the blame in the post mortem. Lead what he has asked for – the nine of hearts!

This holds the first trick to your surprise (and relief) and your second heart clears the suit (to your partner's relief).

I don't think partner would have been impressed by a spade lead which would have resulted in eleven tricks to North-South.

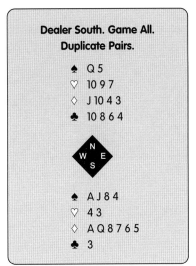

Dealer South. Game All.
Duplicate Pairs.

```
        ♠ Q 5
        ♡ 10 9 7
        ◇ J 10 4 3
        ♣ 10 8 6 4

      N
   W     E
      S

        ♠ A J 8 4
        ♡ 4 3
        ◇ A Q 8 7 6 5
        ♣ 3
```

South	West	North	East
1◇	2♣	3◇[1]	Double[2]
3♠	4♡	Pass	Pass
5◇	Pass	Pass	Double
All Pass			

[1] a weak four-card raise
[2] showing values in the other two suits (majors)

West leads the ♣A, then ♣K.

South has overbid, but can he rescue the situation?

He can afford to go two down (–500) assuming that 4♡ (–620) is a make. The main problem seems to be the lack of entries to dummy.

Dealer South. Game All. Duplicate Pairs.

```
                   ♠ Q 5
                   ♡ 10 9 7
                   ◇ J 10 4 3
                   ♣ 10 8 6 4
        ♠ 10 3                      ♠ K 9 7 6 2
        ♡ K J 8 6          N        ♡ A Q 5 2
        ◇ K 2          W     E      ◇ 9
        ♣ A K Q 9 7        S        ♣ J 5 2
                   ♠ A J 8 4
                   ♡ 4 3
                   ◇ A Q 8 7 6 5
                   ♣ 3
```

South	West	North	East
1◇	2♣	3◇¹	Double²
3♠	4♡	Pass	Pass
5◇	Pass	Pass	Double
All Pass			

¹a weak four-card raise
²showing values in the other two suits (majors)

West leads the ♣A, then ♣K.

Our declarer played off the ace of diamonds hoping for a singleton king, but when that didn't materialise he could only enter dummy on the third round of trumps and, although the spade finesse was right, he still had to lose the fourth spade for three down and –800; one too many.

All we need is an entry to dummy on the second round of trumps, then we can take the spade finesse and ruff two spades. We should give up on the chance of the singleton king, because at most other tables the contract will be 4♡. What really matters is that we score better than –620. The king of spades is likely to be right because of East's first double, so by taking the finesse and ruffing two spade losers we can beat those defending 4♡.

Lead a small trump from hand. West can win, but we can then enter dummy with the jack of diamonds and take a spade finesse. The jack of spades and two spade ruffs in dummy leaves us with nine tricks; –500 against an easy 620 for East-West. A top rather than a bottom.

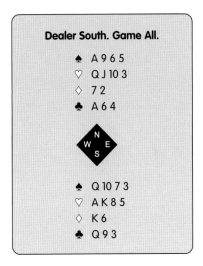

Dealer South. Game All.

   ♠ A 9 6 5
   ♡ Q J 10 3
   ◇ 7 2
   ♣ A 6 4

   ♠ Q 10 7 3
   ♡ A K 8 5
   ◇ K 6
   ♣ Q 9 3

South	West	North	East
1NT¹	Pass	2♣	Double
2♡	Pass	3♡	Pass
4♡	Pass	Pass	Double
All Pass			

¹weak no-trump (12–14)

West leads the ♡6.

East's first double showed clubs, after which North-South bid the normal major-suit game.

 East's double has probably pinpointed most of the values, but unfortunately, when we cash a second trump, he shows out. When we play a small spade from dummy, East takes his king and follows with a second spade, West showing a doubleton. What now?

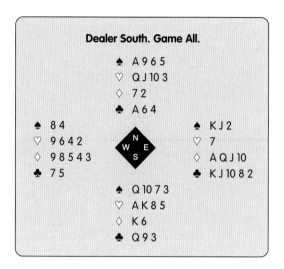

Dealer South. Game All.

```
              ♠ A 9 6 5
              ♡ Q J 10 3
              ◇ 7 2
              ♣ A 6 4
  ♠ 8 4                      ♠ K J 2
  ♡ 9 6 4 2          N       ♡ 7
  ◇ 9 8 5 4 3    W       E   ◇ A Q J 10
  ♣ 7 5              S       ♣ K J 10 8 2
              ♠ Q 10 7 3
              ♡ A K 8 5
              ◇ K 6
              ♣ Q 9 3
```

South	West	North	East
1NT¹	Pass	2♣	Double
2♡	Pass	3♡	Pass
4♡	Pass	Pass	Double
All Pass			

¹weak no-trump (12–14)

West leads the ♡6.

We have little choice but to draw all the trumps; we cannot afford to lose a ruff because we have at least three losers outside trumps. After that it is simply a matter of choosing which minor to play first and with two honours in clubs that must be our first port of call.

A club lead from dummy leaves East helpless. He does indeed hold all the points and is unable to stop our ten tricks. He will probably win the king of clubs and play another club, but we next lead up to the king of diamonds and still have the club suit stopped.

East was justifiably upset after South had claimed, for really his partner should have led his doubleton club (partner's suit) after which declarer is helpless.

Q A good double-dummy problem can be an interesting intellectual exercise. You should always assume 'best defence'. Try the two below.

(1)

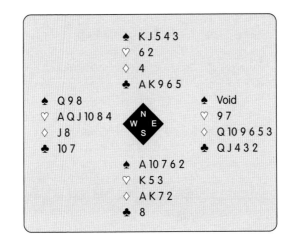

```
              ♠ K J 5 4 3
              ♡ 6 2
              ◇ 4
              ♣ A K 9 6 5
♠ Q 9 8                      ♠ Void
♡ A Q J 10 8 4       N       ♡ 9 7
◇ J 8            W       E    ◇ Q 10 9 6 5 3
♣ 10 7               S       ♣ Q J 4 3 2
              ♠ A 10 7 6 2
              ♡ K 5 3
              ◇ A K 7 2
              ♣ 8
```

Contract: 6♠ by South. Lead: ♣10.

(2)

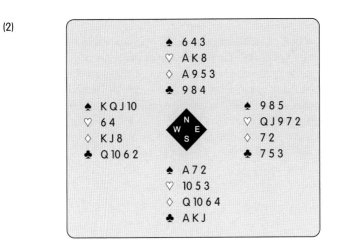

```
              ♠ 6 4 3
              ♡ A K 8
              ◇ A 9 5 3
              ♣ 9 8 4
♠ K Q J 10                   ♠ 9 8 5
♡ 6 4                N       ♡ Q J 9 7 2
◇ K J 8         W       E    ◇ 7 2
♣ Q 10 6 2           S       ♣ 7 5 3
              ♠ A 7 2
              ♡ 10 5 3
              ◇ Q 10 6 4
              ♣ A K J
```

Contract: 3NT by South. Lead: ♠K.

(1) Not a very nice trump break, but nicer things are happening in the other black suit. Without the sight of the two defenders' hands, we would have tried to ruff three times in dummy, but we can see that is not possible. The solution is to take a double ruffing finesse in clubs.

Win the ace of clubs, draw trumps (with the finesse) finishing in dummy. Cash the king of clubs (throwing a heart) and lead the nine of clubs. East will cover but you ruff, cash the ace and king of diamonds (throwing a heart) and ruff a diamond. Now lead the six of clubs and again East has to cover. We can ruff and now have our twelfth trick in the unlikely guise of the five of clubs, so ruff another diamond and cash it – losing just one heart at the end.

(2) We have six top tricks and can easily establish two more in diamonds, but where will the ninth come from? We will have to endplay West, but that will be difficult because if we play diamonds to establish our tricks, West will win the first or second round, cash spades and then return another diamond, leaving us with a club loser at the end.

So we must try to endplay West before establishing our diamonds. Win the ace of spades, cash the ace and king of hearts to remove West's cards in the suit, and now exit with a spade. West wins and cashes two more spades (a heart is thrown from both hands), but now he is left with only minor-suit cards.

A club exit is fatal for we win with the jack and simply establish our two extra winners in diamonds. A diamond exit allows us to force him to win the third round of diamonds and thus eventually he has to lead a club to give us our ninth trick. For example, say he tries the eight of diamonds; we win with the ten, cash the ace, and put him on lead with the king. With only clubs left West has to give us our ninth trick.

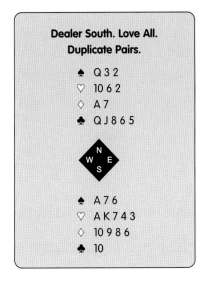

Dealer South. Love All.
Duplicate Pairs.

♠ Q 3 2
♡ 10 6 2
♢ A 7
♣ Q J 8 6 5

N
W E
S

♠ A 7 6
♡ A K 7 4 3
♢ 10 9 8 6
♣ 10

South	West	North	East
1♡	Double	2♡	Pass
Pass	Double	All Pass	

West leads the ♣K, then switches to the ♠4.

The hand would look rather healthy were it not for the rather ominous bidding. West might have led a trump if he had one (certainly at his second lead).

Can we cope with the bad break?

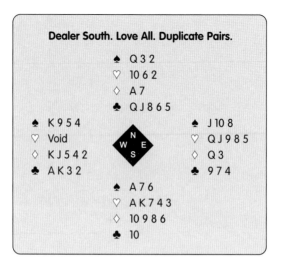

Dealer South. Love All. Duplicate Pairs.

	♠ Q 3 2	
	♡ 10 6 2	
	◇ A 7	
	♣ Q J 8 6 5	
♠ K 9 5 4		♠ J 10 8
♡ Void		♡ Q J 9 8 5
◇ K J 5 4 2		◇ Q 3
♣ A K 3 2		♣ 9 7 4
	♠ A 7 6	
	♡ A K 7 4 3	
	◇ 10 9 8 6	
	♣ 10	

South	West	North	East
1♡	Double	2♡	Pass
Pass	Double	All Pass	

West leads the ♣K, then switches to the ♠4.

If the king of spades is wrong, we will lose two spades, one diamond, one club and surely at least two trumps if not three; this will not be a good score. We have to hope that it is right and work from there.

So we rise with the queen of spades and follow with the queen of clubs discarding a small spade from hand. West wins and plays another spade, which we win, cross to dummy with the ace of diamonds and cash the jack of clubs (throwing a diamond). Now we ruff a spade and exit with a diamond. Whether he wins the queen of diamonds or West overtakes with the king, poor East has only trumps left and will soon have to lead away from ♡QJ98(5) allowing dummy's ten to score (if he leads the queen or jack, then we duck, forcing him to lead again, and clearly any other card allows the ten to win straight away). Three hearts, one ruff, two spades, one club and one diamond add up to eight tricks.

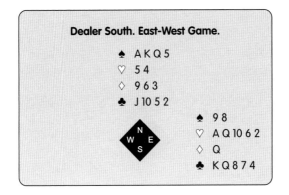

Dealer South. East-West Game.

♠ A K Q 5
♡ 5 4
♢ 9 6 3
♣ J 10 5 2

♠ 9 8
♡ A Q 10 6 2
♢ Q
♣ K Q 8 7 4

South	West	North	East
5◇	Pass	Pass	Double
All Pass			

West leads the ♣A.

When the bidding came round to East, he just couldn't resist the temptation and made a greedy double. Dummy is looking rather good and apologies to partner might be necessary. Still, after partner's lead, all might be well, but how can we best manoeuvre to make sure our side cashes its tricks before discards are taken on the spades in dummy?

What do you play?

A

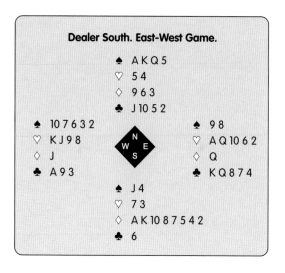

Dealer South. East-West Game.

	North
♠	A K Q 5
♡	5 4
◇	9 6 3
♣	J 10 5 2

West		East	
♠	10 7 6 3 2	♠	9 8
♡	K J 9 8	♡	A Q 10 6 2
◇	J	◇	Q
♣	A 9 3	♣	K Q 8 7 4

	South
♠	J 4
♡	7 3
◇	A K 10 8 7 5 4 2
♣	6

South	West	North	East
5◇	Pass	Pass	Double
All Pass			

West leads the ♣A.

With discards available on the ♠AKQ, we need to cash our tricks in the correct order. If we encourage in clubs partner will probably continue; that will work well if he has only two but if he has three, it will get ruffed and we might have had two heart tricks which will quickly disappear on the top spades? Can we find a more precise defence?

We need partner to hold the king of hearts (or declarer to hold two clubs). If we deny a club holding by playing a small club partner will surely switch to his highest heart which will clear up the situation. Furthermore, if partner does lead the king of hearts we can give him *count* after which he can decide, accurately, which suit needs to be played next (our signal on the king is clearly count because our attitude is known when the king wins the trick!).

So here the defence should be: ace of clubs (East playing the four), king of hearts (East playing the two) and now West knows to continue with another heart, which East can win and try the king of clubs which is ruffed.

These defences are always very tricky, but it is all the more important here because East-West can make 4♡ (not that they are ever likely to be allowed to play there).

Bernard Magee's Bridge Quiz Book

Dealer South. East-West Game.
Teams of Four.

♠ 9
♡ A 6 4 3 2
♢ 7 5 4 2
♣ 8 5 2

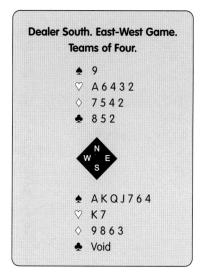

♠ A K Q J 7 6 4
♡ K 7
♢ 9 8 6 3
♣ Void

South	West	North	East
4♠	Pass	Pass	Double
All Pass			

West leads the ♣Q.

Would you open 4♠ on that? Many would open 1♠, but at this vulnerability, it can pay to leave everybody else at the table in the dark – there are two opponents to one partner so the disruption should be greater to the opposition. Of course, the contract might even make!

Yes, with seven spades, two hearts and a diamond if the suit breaks 3-2, we surely have a good chance. Anything to look out for?

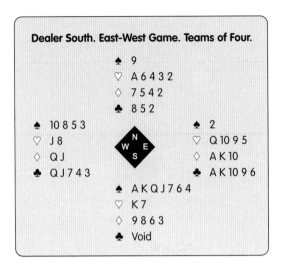

Dealer South. East-West Game. Teams of Four.

```
              ♠ 9
              ♡ A 6 4 3 2
              ◇ 7 5 4 2
              ♣ 8 5 2
♠ 10 8 5 3                    ♠ 2
♡ J 8              N          ♡ Q 10 9 5
◇ Q J          W     E        ◇ A K 10
♣ Q J 7 4 3        S          ♣ A K 10 9 6
              ♠ A K Q J 7 6 4
              ♡ K 7
              ◇ 9 8 6 3
              ♣ Void
```

South	West	North	East
4♠	Pass	Pass	Double
All Pass			

West leads the ♣Q.

With East-West unable to make game (5♣ has three top losers) it is important that we make this.

Naturally, our declarer ruffed the queen of clubs and drew trumps in four rounds. Then, with crossed fingers, he led diamonds. Unfortunately, what he hadn't catered for was that the defence would lead clubs every time they won a trick. By the time he came to lead the third diamond, he had no trumps left and had to settle for one down.

Where did he go wrong?

He overlooked dummy's solitary trump. Yes, if we play diamonds before drawing any trumps, then when we lose that third diamond we can ruff a fourth round of clubs in dummy. Then we can cross to the king of hearts and draw trumps.

The only layouts on which this can go wrong occur when one defender holds a doubleton diamond and a singleton heart, either 2-1-2-8 or 3-1-2-7, when drawing trumps would have worked after all. But these are unlikely and even supposing West had passed East's double with such a hand, he would more than likely have led his singleton heart at trick one.

Dealer South. Love All.

```
                  ♠ J 8 5 2
                  ♡ Q J 10 4
                  ◇ 7 6
                  ♣ A K 6
♠ Void
♡ 9 8 6 5 3            N
◇ Q 10 8 2         W       E
♣ Q J 10 9            S
```

South	West	North	East
1♠	Pass	3♠	Pass
4♠	Pass	Pass	Double
All Pass			

West leads the ♣Q to dummy's ♣A, partner playing the ♣3 and declarer the ♣2; the ♡Q is won by partner's ♡K and he now plays king, ace and another trump.

South, who it seems thus far, must have opened extremely light, still could not resist the temptation of game, and our partner could not resist the taste of blood. We have three discards to make: the first two seem simple – a heart and a club – but the third?

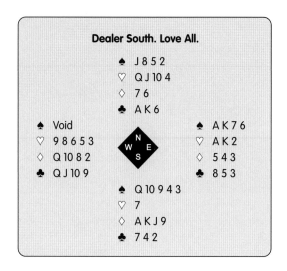

Dealer South. Love All.

	♠ J 8 5 2	
	♡ Q J 10 4	
	◊ 7 6	
	♣ A K 6	

♠ Void		♠ A K 7 6
♡ 9 8 6 5 3		♡ A K 2
◊ Q 10 8 2		◊ 5 4 3
♣ Q J 10 9		♣ 8 5 3

	♠ Q 10 9 4 3	
	♡ 7	
	◊ A K J 9	
	♣ 7 4 2	

South	West	North	East
1♠	Pass	3♠	Pass
4♠	Pass	Pass	Double
All Pass			

West leads the ♣Q to dummy's ♣A, partner playing the ♣3 and declarer the ♣2; the ♡Q is won by partner's ♡K and he now plays king, ace and another trump.

This is an awkward hand. We have a pretty good idea of declarer's hand now: he does not hold the ace of hearts and so must hold all the other high cards. He must also have good distribution. With six spades and a singleton heart 4♠ is cold. If declarer has a doubleton heart, he will be one off, but this seems unlikely (with only ten points, South is more likely to be 5-1-4-3 than 5-2-4-2), so we assume he has a singleton.

Your first two 'easy' discards are the three of hearts and the nine of clubs. Now if we throw a heart, declarer will be able to establish the fourth heart in dummy. If we throw a diamond then if declarer holds four diamonds he can establish the fourth by ruffing. On the other hand if we discard a club then we will set up the suit if declarer holds four clubs or even three clubs to the eight. Not good!

Any clues? Partner's three of clubs is the important card. With a doubleton he would have petered, so this would suggest that East holds three clubs and that South's shape is 5-1-4-3.

Thus we cannot throw a heart or a diamond safely and should hope that partner holds the eight of clubs. Throw the ten of clubs.

Dealer West. Love All.

```
          ♠ Q J 8 7
          ♡ 10 8 3 2
          ◇ 4
          ♣ A Q 8 3
               N
            W     E
               S
          ♠ K 10 9 4
          ♡ A 4
          ◇ A 6 5 3
          ♣ J 4 2
```

South	West	North	East
	1◇	Double	2◇
4♠	Pass	Pass	Double
All Pass			

West leads the ◇K.

We have stretched a little here and, worse luck, we have been found out! A pity partner did not have a little more for his take-out double. Can we extricate ourselves from the mire?

It looks as if East has some trumps, but why did West not lead a trump? Surely that was the obvious lead?

A

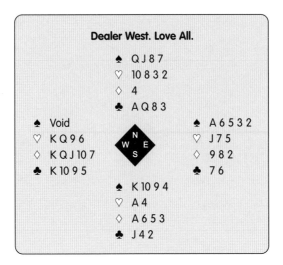

Dealer West. Love All.

```
                    ♠ Q J 8 7
                    ♡ 10 8 3 2
                    ◇ 4
                    ♣ A Q 8 3
    ♠ Void                          ♠ A 6 5 3 2
    ♡ K Q 9 6         N            ♡ J 7 5
    ◇ K Q J 10 7   W     E         ◇ 9 8 2
    ♣ K 10 9 5         S            ♣ 7 6
                    ♠ K 10 9 4
                    ♡ A 4
                    ◇ A 6 5 3
                    ♣ J 4 2
```

South	West	North	East
	1◇	Double	2◇
4♠	Pass	Pass	Double
All Pass			

West leads the ◇K.

Partner is a little light for his take-out double, but he was not the only one up to some tricks; East has chosen to raise diamonds rather than bid 1♠ with at least four cards in the suit.

Short on high cards, our only hope is a cross-ruff and for this to succeed we need trumps to be 5-0, a distinct possibility considering that West failed to lead a trump. We need six trump tricks, three aces and the queen of clubs. It requires precise timing: we have to finesse in clubs as well as ruff diamonds; furthermore we must keep East off lead.

Win the ace of diamonds, ruff a diamond, and lead the ten of hearts which East covers and we win with the ace. Now a club finesse and exit with the eight of hearts. Our luck is in; East is out of high hearts and West has to win. He exits with another heart which we ruff in hand, ruff a diamond and cash the ace of clubs – that makes seven tricks for us and just one for them. Poor old East has only trumps left.

We continue with our fourth heart; East cannot ruff high, or we will make three more high trumps in hand, so he ruffs low and we overruff. Now the last diamond is ruffed high in dummy and East is still stymied – 4♠ doubled and made.

Bernard Magee's Bridge Quiz Book

Q BRIDGE TRIVIA

1. What can be Double, Free, Chinese or Deep?

2. What is a Lightner Double?

3. How much is the insult worth after making a redoubled contract?

4. What is a Striped-tail Ape Double?

5. What can be Kock-Werner, SOS or Rosenkranz?

6. Which are the two most likely hand patterns? (Hand patterns show the lengths of suit in a hand – eg 7-2-2-2 would describe a hand with one seven card suit and three two card suits.)

7. What is a Co-operative Double?

8. How many cards in partner's suit does a Support Double show?

9. What does the term 'Scrambling' mean?

10. A bid of 2NT over an opponent's double of partner's one-of-a-suit opening is often played as a limit raise in opener's suit, leaving a direct raise to three as pre-emptive. What is the name of this convention?

11. What is the difference between DEPO and DIPO?

12. Which is the odd one out: Squeeze, Negative, Dummy, Lead or Raise?

13. What is Double-barrelled Stayman?

14. What is a 'Double Elimination' Knock-out Tournament?

15. Which is worth more at Duplicate, non-vulnerable, 5♡ doubled and made or 2♡ doubled and made with two overtricks?

16. Which of the following is not a type of double? Incredible, Rosenkranz, Delayed, Lightner, Elephant.

17. What is a Double Squeeze?

18. What is a Double Negative?

19. What happens when a player makes an inadmissible double or redouble?

20. What is a 'Wriggle'?

A ANSWERS TO BRIDGE TRIVIA

1. Finesses.
2. A double of a slam contract asking for an 'out of the ordinary' lead, most commonly made when holding a void suit.
3. 100 above the line.
4. A double of a game contract by a defender who believes his opponents will make a slam – the doubled contract with overtricks scores less than the slam. If redoubled the doubler has to flee to his long suit like a striped-tail ape.
5. Redoubles.
6. 4-4-3-2 occurs in 21.6% of hands and 5-3-3-2 is the second most likely, occurring in 15.5%.
7. A double that gives partner the option to pass for penalties or to bid on.
8. Three.
9. Searching for a sensible place to play.
10. Developed by Alan Truscott, this convention carries his name in England but is popularly known as Jordan in the USA.
11. Both are conventions to deal with intervention over Blackwood. DEPO stands for Double = Even number of aces; Pass = Odd number of aces. DIPO stands for Double = 1 ace; Pass = 0 aces.
12. Lead – the others may be preceded by 'double'.
13. A combination of non-forcing and game-forcing Stayman, using both 2♣ and 2◇ as Staymanic (searching for a 4-4 major fit).
14. A knock-out tournament in which a team is eliminated only after it has lost two matches.
15. 2♡ doubled +2 = 670 (5♡ doubled = 650).
16. Elephant.
17. A squeeze on both opponents (it involves three suits).
18. A bid or rebid which expresses a second negative, usually showing 0–3 points with no ace or king.
19. The call is cancelled and the offender may replace any call in its stead, but his partner must pass at his turn to bid, for the rest of the auction.
20. A method of escaping from a doubled contract, by bidding a short suit and then redoubling, asking partner to bid one of the other suits.

Chapter 5

Teams of Four

A form of Duplicate Bridge which involves comparison scoring (translated into International Match Points, IMPs) with your team-mates, greatly reducing the need for overtricks. This means that the play is similar to Rubber Bridge, the aim being to secure the contract rather than to maximise the number of tricks. As in Duplicate Pairs, there are plenty of conventions; the bidding tends to be aggressive as there are handsome dividends for bidding and making game contracts.

Dealer South. Game All. Teams of Four.

♠ A Q 4
♡ 10 8 6
♦ Q J 10 9
♣ 10 6 2

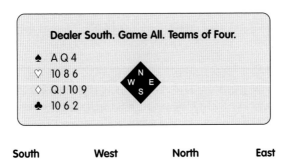

South	West	North	East
3NT	All Pass		

A nice and simple auction, the only bid being the 'gambling 3NT' which usually shows a long and solid seven-card minor with very little outside.

What should we lead?

A

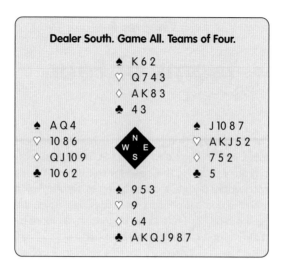

Dealer South. Game All. Teams of Four.

```
                ♠ K 6 2
                ♡ Q 7 4 3
                ◇ A K 8 3
                ♣ 4 3
    ♠ A Q 4                      ♠ J 10 8 7
    ♡ 10 8 6          N          ♡ A K J 5 2
    ◇ Q J 10 9    W       E      ◇ 7 5 2
    ♣ 10 6 2          S          ♣ 5
                ♠ 9 5 3
                ♡ 9
                ◇ 6 4
                ♣ A K Q J 9 8 7
```

South	West	North	East
3NT	All Pass		

We have no idea what dummy will look like, hence the name of the convention – the gambling 3NT. We do know that there is a chance that, if we do not take our tricks quickly, declarer might already have nine.

Try the ace of spades and take a look at dummy – it can't do that much harm for South is very unlikely to hold the king of spades. Now we can see that indeed it does look as though declarer has nine tricks and our only chance is a switch to the ten of hearts. Declarer covers the ten, but our partner is on the ball and after winning his king he continues with a small heart to our eight and then another back to his now established suit puts declarer two down.

Bernard Magee's Bridge Quiz Book

Dealer East. Game All.
Teams of Four.

```
        ♠ Q 4 2
        ♡ 7 2
        ◇ A K Q 5 3 2
        ♣ 8 3

             N
         W       E
             S

        ♠ A 3
        ♡ A K 3
        ◇ 10 8 7 6
        ♣ A 10 5 4
```

South	West	North	East
			1♠¹
Pass	2♠	3◇	Pass
3NT	All Pass		

¹five-card major

West leads the ♠10 which runs to your ♠A.

This would have been better played by partner with the spade lead running round to the queen, but still it does not look that bad! Six diamonds, three aces and a king – is life really that easy?

A

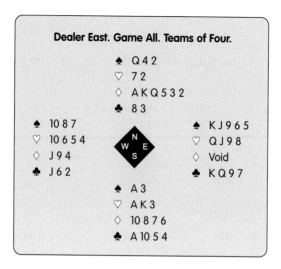

Dealer East. Game All. Teams of Four.

	♠ Q42	
	♡ 72	
	◇ AKQ532	
	♣ 83	

♠ 1087   ♠ KJ965
♡ 10654   ♡ QJ98
◇ J94   ◇ Void
♣ J62   ♣ KQ97

	♠ A3	
	♡ AK3	
	◇ 10876	
	♣ A1054	

South	West	North	East
			1♠¹
Pass	2♠	3◇	Pass
3NT	All Pass		

¹five card major

West leads the ♠10 which runs to your ♠A.

At the table, South won the lead, played a diamond to the ace, East showing out and it was only at this point that he paused for thought – Agh! Blocked! Yes, and suddenly he was down to four diamonds, three aces and a king. Inspirationally, South called for the queen of spades from dummy. East won this, but unfortunately for South, he was not after just four spade tricks and rather than allowing declarer to throw his fourth diamond on the extra spades, he switched to clubs and our South was down.

You do not need all six diamond tricks so, if you notice the blockage before you play your first diamond, the answer is simple: lead the ten of diamonds and run it. If West covers, win, return to hand with the ace of hearts and run the eight of diamonds; if this is covered we can come back to the seven of diamonds and win the fourth round of the suit in dummy. Of course, if East wins the first diamond with the jack, he cannot harm us as a spade lead from his side is harmless.

The auctions in Teams of Four matches are like a mixture of Duplicate and Rubber. There are some of the conventions of the former, but a little less aggression on partscore deals because there is no need to scrap for every ten points. Getting into the auction is still important, but not so much so that great risks need to be taken. The one area of Teams' bidding where caution is thrown to the wind is in game bidding; thin games can pay great dividends.

Try these problems as South:

(1) Dealer West. Love All.

♠ 6 2
♡ A Q 5 4
◇ K Q 9 7 6
♣ 5 2

South	West	North	East
	Pass	1NT[1]	Pass
2♣	Pass	2♠	Pass
?			

[1]strong no-trump (15–17)

(2) Dealer South. Game All.

♠ 9 7 3
♡ K 5 4 3
◇ Q J 7 6 3
♣ 2

South	West	North	East
Pass	Pass	1♡[1]	Pass
2♡	Pass	3♣	Pass
?			

[1]four card major

(3) Dealer West. Love All.

♠ A 5
♡ K 2
◇ Q J 3 2
♣ A 9 7 6 5

South	West	North	East
	Pass	1♡	Pass
2♣	Pass	2◇	Pass
?			

(4) Dealer West. East-West Game.

♠ K 7 6 5
♡ A 7 4
◇ J 8 4 2
♣ 7 3

South	West	North	East
	1♡	2♠[1]	3♣
?			

[1]weak jump overcall

(5) Dealer West. Love All.

♠ A K 3 2
♡ J 6 3 2
◇ Q 9 4 2
♣ 7

South	West	North	East
	2♡[1]	Pass	Pass
?			

[1]weak two

(1) 3◇ – Eleven points opposite a strong no-trump and one's thoughts after the discovery that there is no fit in a major turn directly to 3NT. Why bother 'telling the opponents to lead clubs'? But at Teams when the difference between 5◇ making and 3NT+1 is minimal, it is important to find the best game. What if partner has no club stop, say: ♠AK54 ♡K72 ◇A1032 ♣Q3? Even if he holds one club stop, 5◇ could still be the safer game.

(2) 4♡ – In Teams bridge, the games are all important – that is often where matches are won and lost. Here partner is making a game try, asking for help in the suit bid, and although we are rather short of points, our hand fits perfectly with only one loser in clubs and we should certainly bid game. North's hand is likely to be something like: ♠AK2 ♡AQ72 ◇K5 ♣J843.

(3) 2♠ followed by 3◇ – We have two choices: to support diamonds or to bid 3NT. Bidding 3NT would be precipitous, especially with only a single spade stop. Best is to support diamonds, but 3◇ would not be forcing, so that is no good. The solution is to bid the fourth suit, which is not a natural bid but simply a way to progress the bidding at a sensibly low level. When we rebid in diamonds, we show primary support and force the partnership to game.

(4) 4♠ – This is Teams, but we are still allowed to sacrifice. Here, even if partner has just the ace of spades in his six-card suit, we will make seven or eight tricks, which will be –500 at worst. A game from their side, however, will lose the ace of hearts, one spade and ... possibly one more trick? –620 for 4♡. There are very few layouts where 4♠ is wrong. Partner is likely to hold something like: ♠A108432 ♡6 ◇A65 ♣862.

(5) Pass – Partner is short in hearts, but has not doubled for take-out, why? Because he is not very strong and it is East who actually holds the majority of the outstanding points. When re-opening on light hands, we do so in order to protect partner, to keep the bidding alive when our partner could not find a bid. Here, East might hold ♠Q984 ♡7 ◇AK53 ♣A1062 and it is he who will be hoping that we re-open the bidding.

Dealer South. Game All.
Teams of Four.

```
              ♠  10 9 3
              ♡  8 4 2
              ◇  5 2
              ♣  A K Q 4 3

                   N
                W     E
                   S

              ♠  K Q J 8 4
              ♡  A K 7 5
              ◇  10
              ♣  J 7 2
```

South	West	North	East
1♠	2◇	3♣¹	4◇²
4♠	All Pass		

¹suggesting spade support as well as clubs
²pre-emptive

West leads the ◇A, then ◇K.

A typically competitive auction, with East doing his best to disrupt our bidding by jumping a level on surely by far the poorest hand at the table. Have we been forced too far? It does not appear so. It all looks rather comfortable. Too comfortable? No need for overtricks, so can we make sure of our contract?

Plan the play.

A

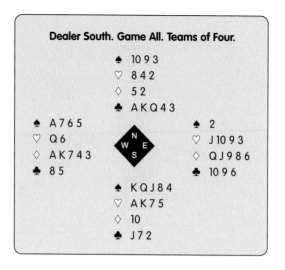

Dealer South. Game All. Teams of Four.

	♠ 10 9 3	
	♡ 8 4 2	
	◇ 5 2	
	♣ A K Q 4 3	
♠ A 7 6 5		♠ 2
♡ Q 6		♡ J 10 9 3
◇ A K 7 4 3		◇ Q J 9 8 6
♣ 8 5		♣ 10 9 6
	♠ K Q J 8 4	
	♡ A K 7 5	
	◇ 10	
	♣ J 7 2	

South	West	North	East
1♠	2◇	3♣[1]	4◇[2]
4♠	All Pass		

[1] suggesting spade support as well as clubs
[2] pre-emptive

West leads the ◇A, then ◇K.

A lazy declarer ruffs and tries to draw trumps but after the second round is ducked and East discards a diamond, it is too late. Declarer cannot continue trumps, for West will win and force declarer to use his last trump to ruff a diamond. But if declarer tries clubs West simply ruffs the third round and cashes the ace of spades and there is no way back to dummy.

The solution is rather simple: throw a heart (not a club) on the king of diamonds instead of ruffing. This keeps control of the trump suit because West is unable to continue diamonds profitably for we can ruff in dummy. After any other switch, we simply draw trumps, losing only two diamonds and the ace of trumps.

Why not discard a club? Because West will switch to clubs and then continue clubs after winning the third round of trumps. Now there is no way to draw trumps and enjoy the clubs.

The discard of a heart at trick two is a safety play; it will give up an overtrick when trumps are 3-2, but playing Teams, we need not worry about that – the safety of the contract is uppermost.

Dealer South. Love All. Teams of Four.

```
                    ♠ A 6 3
                    ♡ K J 7
                    ◇ J 10 5
                    ♣ K J 5 2
   ♠ K J
   ♡ Q 10 4              N
   ◇ A 7 6 4 2      W        E
   ♣ Q 10 3              S
```

South	West	North	East
1NT[1]	Pass	3NT	All Pass

[1]weak no-trump (12–14)

West leads the ◇4 to dummy's ◇10 and partner's ◇K; he returns the ◇9, and we let declarer's ◇Q hold the trick; after a little thought declarer leads the ♣4.

What is there to think about? Things do not look hopeful.

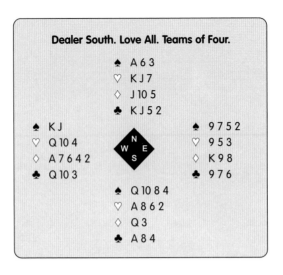

Dealer South. Love All. Teams of Four.

	♠ A 6 3	
	♡ K J 7	
	◇ J 10 5	
	♣ K J 5 2	
♠ K J		♠ 9 7 5 2
♡ Q 10 4		♡ 9 5 3
◇ A 7 6 4 2		◇ K 9 8
♣ Q 10 3		♣ 9 7 6
	♠ Q 10 8 4	
	♡ A 8 6 2	
	◇ Q 3	
	♣ A 8 4	

South	West	North	East
1NT[1]	Pass	3NT	All Pass

¹weak no-trump (12–14)

West leads the ◇4 to dummy's ◇10 and partner's ◇K; he returns the ◇9, and we let declarer's ◇Q hold the trick; after a little thought declarer leads the ♠4.

The only real thing to think over is how we might push declarer off course. From our hand, he seems to have no real choice but to hit upon the winning line; with us holding both tens in the key suits, it is clear that there is no two-way finesse so he is likely to finish with nine or ten tricks by way of two finesses (in hearts and clubs).

But why is he playing a spade? To test all the avenues open to him. Perhaps this is our chance? If declarer has ♠Q10 in hand we might just be able to guide him away from safety. Unfortunately we needed to think of this before he led the spade (thinking with a singleton is frowned upon!). Did you?

Yes, on the spade lead drop the king in tempo and declarer will have a smile on his face, happy at having found that elusive extra chance, only to be in tears on the next round when we win our jack and cash our three diamond tricks.

Dealer South. Game All.
Teams of Four.

♠ Q J 8 5
♡ A K 7 4
♢ K 5 3
♣ 6 3

```
      N
   W     E
      S
```

♠ A K 9 3 2
♡ J 9 3
♢ 9 4 2
♣ A K

South	West	North	East
1♠	Pass	2♡	Pass
3♡	Pass	4♠	All Pass

West leads the ♣Q.

In the bidding, North was planning a Delayed Game Raise to show four-card support and 13–15 points and thus he bid his hearts first. Even after South's raise there was never going to be a mix-up over which suit to play in because North was firmly in control of the auction and he duly fulfilled his plan by bidding 4♠.

An unfortunate duplication of shape in the minors makes this contract rather more difficult than it might have been. Any ideas?

A

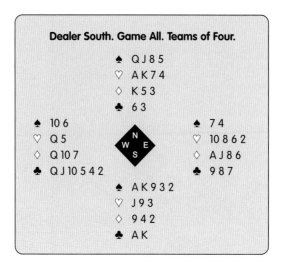

Dealer South. Game All. Teams of Four.

```
                    ♠ Q J 8 5
                    ♡ A K 7 4
                    ◇ K 5 3
                    ♣ 6 3
   ♠ 10 6                              ♠ 7 4
   ♡ Q 5          N                    ♡ 10 8 6 2
   ◇ Q 10 7     W   E                  ◇ A J 8 6
   ♣ Q J 10 5 4 2    S                 ♣ 9 8 7
                    ♠ A K 9 3 2
                    ♡ J 9 3
                    ◇ 9 4 2
                    ♣ A K
```

South	West	North	East
1♠	Pass	2♡	Pass
3♡	Pass	4♠	All Pass

West leads the ♣Q.

If the ace of diamonds is right then declarer will always make, but we would like better than 50/50 odds. A 3-3 heart break could supply the tenth trick, but if we let West get the lead we will lose three diamond tricks if the ace is wrong. There are also endplay chances if the hearts break 4-2. So we must play to maximise our chances whilst keeping West off lead.

We win the club lead and cash a second club, then two round of trumps to which both opponents follow. Now the jack of hearts. This is covered by West, so we win the ace and cross back to hand in trumps. Now lead the nine of hearts which runs to East, but he is endplayed: if he has no more hearts he either gives us a ruff and discard or opens up the diamonds; if the hearts are 3-3, we are home anyway; and if he has two more hearts he cannot lead away from ♡86 into dummy's ♡K7.

A very neat avoidance play.

We can only fail if West holds the queen, ten and eight of hearts as well as East holding the ace of diamonds, and if you are having that kind of day, I would stop playing!

Dealer North. Love All.
Teams of Four.

```
              ♠ A 8 7 2
              ♡ 5 4
              ◊ A Q 7
              ♣ A K Q 4

                   N
               W       E
                   S

              ♠ K J 6 3
              ♡ Q J 3
              ◊ 9 2
              ♣ J 7 6 3
```

South	West	North	East
		1♣	Pass
1♠	Pass	4♠	All Pass

West leads the ♡K, ♡A and a third heart which runs to our ♡Q.

How should we play trumps? How should we play the contract?

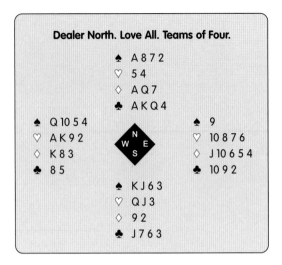

Dealer North. Love All. Teams of Four.

	♠ A 8 7 2	
	♡ 5 4	
	◇ A Q 7	
	♣ A K Q 4	

♠ Q 10 5 4		♠ 9
♡ A K 9 2	N	♡ 10 8 7 6
◇ K 8 3	W E	◇ J 10 6 5 4
♣ 8 5	S	♣ 10 9 2

	♠ K J 6 3	
	♡ Q J 3	
	◇ 9 2	
	♣ J 7 6 3	

South	West	North	East
		1♣	Pass
1♠	Pass	4♠	All Pass

West leads the ♡K, ♡A and a third heart which runs to our ♡Q.

The first is a slightly misleading question, for how we play trumps depends on how many tricks we need from the suit. If we have a loser in diamonds, we cannot afford a trump loser and would thus play a spade to the ace and finesse in the usual way. But if, on the other hand, we do not lose a diamond, we can afford to make a safety play in the trump suit.

So, we must take a diamond finesse first. When the diamond queen holds the trick we know how to play the trump suit.

We start with a small spade towards the king and when East plays the nine on the first round we win with the king and play another trump towards table, inserting the eight if West plays low. If East does not play the nine, ten or queen on the first round we still put up the king, then follow with a trump to the ace and lead towards the jack if necessary. (There is nothing we can do if West holds Q109x, but if he holds Q9xx or Q10xx, then extra care rewards declarer with his contract.)

Dealer East. Love All. Teams of Four.

```
              ♠ Q 7 2
              ♡ 10 8 2
              ◇ K Q 4
              ♣ K J 10 2
                              ♠ 5 3
            N                 ♡ K J 9 4
        W       E             ◇ J 8 7 6
            S                 ♣ A 9 8
```

South	West	North	East
			Pass
1◇	Pass	2♣	Pass
2NT¹	Pass	3NT	All Pass

¹15–17 points

West leads the ♠J which runs to South's ♠A;
declarer leads the ♣6 to partner's ♣5 and dummy's ♣J.

North-South's system precluded North from making a natural 2NT response so he had to settle for the unattractive 2♣.

Diamonds seem to be lying well for declarer; with five to the ace he will pick up the suit for no losers. What do we do?

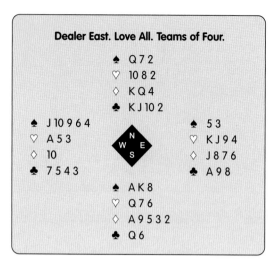

Dealer East. Love All. Teams of Four.

```
                    ♠ Q 7 2
                    ♡ 10 8 2
                    ◇ K Q 4
                    ♣ K J 10 2
  ♠ J 10 9 6 4              ♠ 5 3
  ♡ A 5 3          N         ♡ K J 9 4
  ◇ 10         W     E       ◇ J 8 7 6
  ♣ 7 5 4 3         S        ♣ A 9 8
                    ♠ A K 8
                    ♡ Q 7 6
                    ◇ A 9 5 3 2
                    ♣ Q 6
```

South	West	North	East
			Pass
1◇	Pass	2♣	Pass
2NT¹	Pass	3NT	All Pass

¹15–17 points

West leads the ♠J which runs to South's ♠A;
declarer leads the ♣6 to partner's ♣5 and dummy's ♣J.

The two hands we can see contain twenty points and South has shown 15–17 in the bidding, so partner can have five points at the most, of which one is the jack of spades. If he holds the king of spades, declarer holds the rest and has plenty of tricks. Queens in clubs and hearts are useless too. How about the ace of diamonds? Again declarer can make three clubs, two diamonds, three spades and two hearts – ten tricks.

Finally what about the ace of hearts? Declarer will have eight tricks plus three club tricks after we have won the ace. Notice that, if we do not win the club straightaway, declarer will run for home with nine tricks. So we must win the first club and make use of the ace of hearts in partner's hand by means of what is called a 'surrounding play' – lead the jack of hearts. If declarer covers this, partner will win and lead another heart through North's ♡108 to our ♡K9; if declarer does not cover we simply play a low heart to partner's ace and another one to our king nets four tricks in the suit.

Four heart tricks and the ace of clubs – one down, well done!

Bernard Magee's Bridge Quiz Book

Q

Dealer West. Love All.
Teams of Four.

♠ A K 4
♡ 7 5 3 2
◊ A 9 3
♣ A Q 8

```
      N
   W     E
      S
```

♠ Q J 10 7 3
♡ 4
◊ K 6 5
♣ J 10 9 5

South	West	North	East
	1♡	Double	2♡
3♠	Pass	4♠	All Pass

West leads the ♡A, followed by ♡K.

Over South's aggressive 3♠ bid, North did not hesitate to bid game, despite his balanced hand.

There do not seem to be too many problems. Is there something to be wary of?

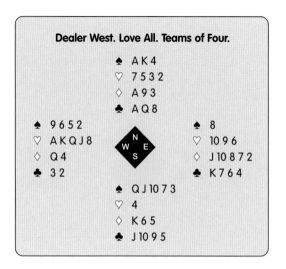

Dealer West. Love All. Teams of Four.

		♠ A K 4		
		♡ 7 5 3 2		
		◇ A 9 3		
		♣ A Q 8		
♠ 9 6 5 2				♠ 8
♡ A K Q J 8				♡ 10 9 6
◇ Q 4				◇ J 10 8 7 2
♣ 3 2				♣ K 7 6 4
		♠ Q J 10 7 3		
		♡ 4		
		◇ K 6 5		
		♣ J 10 9 5		

South	West	North	East
	1♡	Double	2♡
3♠	Pass	4♠	All Pass

West leads the ♡A, followed by ♡K.

Declarer ruffed the second heart, drew trumps and finessed in clubs, placing West with the king for his opening bid. Unfortunately, East won, returned a heart and with no trumps left West was able to cash his hearts for two down.

Just a little more care and the contract is secure. It was a mistake to ruff the second heart. Suppose we discard a diamond instead and ruff the third heart. Then East will have no more hearts left when he gets in with the king of clubs and we can win his minor-suit return and claim ten tricks.

A deceptively simple play; much more easily found in no-trump contracts.

Q BRIDGE TRIVIA

1. In Teams championships, the tables where the two halves of a team play are often referred to as in the Open room and the Closed room. What do these terms mean?

2. From which country did the famous Blue Team come?

3. Where were the 1995 Bridge World Championships held?

4. What does a Pivot Teams Competition entail?

5. In big national and international team competitions, what is the usual size of squad (players only) for each team?

6. What is 'Board-a-match'?

7. What does IMP stand for?

8. What is the Venice Cup?

9. What is the chance that six cards in a suit are divided 3-3 between the defenders?

10. What is a Speedball?

11. What is the largest number of IMPs you can gain on one hand?

12. What does HUM stand for?

13. Which are the two most highly prized Teams trophies in the American bridge calendar?

14. In tournament bridge, what might one appeal against?

15. What is a Phantom Sacrifice?

16. In which event are you likely to play more boards against each team: a Multiple Teams or a Swiss Teams?

17. In what years did the 'Sharif Bridge Circus' operate – a team of bridge professionals, headed by Omar Sharif, touring around the world playing bridge matches?

18. What is a Double Game Swing?

19. How is a tie in a knock-out teams match usually resolved?

20. In which year was the annual match between the House of Commons and the House of Lords initiated?

A ANSWERS TO BRIDGE TRIVIA

1. Spectators are allowed in the Open room but not in the Closed.

2. Italy.

3. Beijing (Peking).

4. Each member of the team must partner each other player in the team for a certain number of boards.

5. Six.

6. A method of playing multiple teams in which each board has a value of one point (also called 'Point-a-board').

7. International Match Point.

8. The prize for the women's bridge world championship contested every two years.

9. 35.5%.

10. An event played with a very short time limit, usually five minutes or less per board rather than the usual 71/2 to 8 minutes.

11. 24.

12. Highly Unusual Methods (as regards bidding conventions).

13. Spingold Trophy and Vanderbilt Cup.

14. A director's ruling.

15. A sacrifice bid made against a contract that would have been defeated.

16. Swiss Teams.

17. 1967–70.

18. A board on which both pairs of a team bid and make a game (sitting East-West at one table and North-South at the other).

19. By playing extra boards (the number depends on the regulations of the specific event).

20. 1975.

Chapter 6

High Levels

L ike doubled contracts, misguessing at the five-, six- or seven-level can be rather expensive. A missed slam, or a failing 5♡ when 4♡ was making; all are costly at whatever form of bridge. Once more the heat is on ... This trivia section deals with the personalities of bridge – old and new.

Dealer South. East-West Game.

♠ Void
♡ 10 8 5 3
♢ J 9 8 5 4
♣ A K 10 4

South	West	North	East
1♠	Pass	2NT¹	Pass
4♣²	Pass	4♢³	Pass
5♣²	Pass	5NT	Pass
7♠	Pass	Pass	Double
All Pass			

¹game-forcing with spade support
²splinter, showing shortage and subsequently (5♣) a void
³cue bid

Partner's double suggests that he has a void somewhere, but in which suit? What should we lead?

A

```
           Dealer South. East-West Game.
                    ♠ J 7 5 4 3
                    ♡ A K 7 4 2
                    ◇ A
                    ♣ 6 3
     ♠ Void                        ♠ 9 8 2
     ♡ 10 8 5 3       N            ♡ Void
     ◇ J 9 8 5 4   W     E         ◇ 7 6 3
     ♣ A K 10 4       S            ♣ Q J 9 8 7 5 2
                    ♠ A K Q 10 6
                    ♡ Q J 9 6
                    ◇ K Q 10 2
                    ♣ Void
```

South	West	North	East
1♠	Pass	2NT¹	Pass
4♣²	Pass	4◇³	Pass
5♣²	Pass	5NT	Pass
7♠	Pass	Pass	Double
All Pass			

¹game-forcing with spade support
²splinter, showing shortage and subsequently (5♣) a void
³cue bid

North-South had a reasonable sequence to the grand slam, finishing with the Grand-Slam Force which South not unreasonably accepted! It is a very good contract, but partner's double is a blessing and if we guess the right lead, all our opponents' bidding will have been in vain.

The clue is to look back through the auction – partner would probably have doubled the suit that he wanted led if given a chance, but over 4◇, he kept quiet. This is not a failsafe argument, but it is certainly one that sways the odds significantly in favour of a heart.

The heart lead brings a grim look to declarer's face, which turns grimmer still as partner ruffs the lead to take the contract one down.

One might have thought about leading the ace of clubs because sometimes the opponents tell lies in their auction to disrupt the defence. But in this case, the club void is central to the auction – why go near 7♠ with a singleton?

Bernard Magee's Bridge Quiz Book

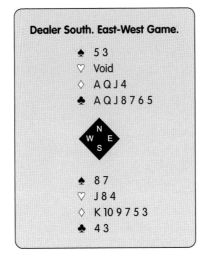

Dealer South. East-West Game.

```
              ♠  5 3
              ♡  Void
              ◇  A Q J 4
              ♣  A Q J 8 7 6 5

                    N
                 W     E
                    S

              ♠  8 7
              ♡  J 8 4
              ◇  K 10 9 7 5 3
              ♣  4 3
```

South	West	North	East
2◇¹	Double	5◇	5♡
6◇	6♡	7◇	Double
All Pass			

¹weak two, six card suit and 4–9 points

West leads the ♡A.

Wow! Did anybody know what was going on, who was sacrificing against whom? As it is, it seems that we were the ones meant to be sacrificing, but on the ace of hearts lead, we have very serious chances of making our contract.

What is the best line for thirteen tricks?

A

Dealer South. East-West Game.

```
                ♠ 5 3
                ♡ Void
                ◇ A Q J 4
                ♣ A Q J 8 7 6 5

  ♠ A Q 10 4           ♠ K J 9 6 2
  ♡ A K Q      N       ♡ 10 9 7 6 5 3 2
  ◇ 8 2     W     E    ◇ 6
  ♣ K 10 9 2    S      ♣ Void

                ♠ 8 7
                ♡ J 8 4
                ◇ K 10 9 7 5 3
                ♣ 4 3
```

South	West	North	East
2◇¹	Double	5◇	5♡
6◇	6♡	7◇	Double
All Pass			

¹weak two, six card suit and 4–9 points

West leads the ♡A.

If we ruff, draw trumps and take a club finesse, we will make if clubs are 2-2 or 3-1 with the king right and trumps 2-1. With trumps 3-0, we cannot afford to draw all the trumps because there will not be enough entries for two finesses. And what about a 4-0 break in clubs? Again we are short of entries.

There is an important safety play available: we should take the first club finesse after only the first round of trumps to facilitate the entry position. Ruff the heart lead with the jack and play a trump to the ten (all following), now a club to the jack. East shows out, but he has no more trumps and we have a complete picture. Overtake the queen of diamonds with the king, take a second club finesse, cash the ace of clubs and ruff the fourth club. We still have the ace of diamonds as an entry for the long clubs – 7◇ doubled and made.

Any declarer bemoaning the distribution when he goes down in 7◇ should take a look at dummy – with that distribution in one hand why should there not be a similar distribution in another?

Below are two hands which require you to make a decision at a rather uncomfortable level. Try them out, but beware: if you get them wrong, they might well cost a lot of points! You are East in both cases.

(1) Dealer South. Love All.

♠	10 9 6
♡	7 6 4
♢	8 6 2
♣	J 5 4 3

South	West	North	East
1♢	Double	4♢¹	Pass
Pass	Double	Pass	?

¹weak; pre-emptive.

What do you say?
A bad hand!
OK, what do you bid?
Bid on that?!
Well?

(2) Dealer West. East-West Game.

♠	K 5 4 3
♡	K 2
♢	K J 5 4 3
♣	Q 7

South	West	North	East
	1♡	3♣¹	Double²
4♣	Pass	Pass	?

¹weak jump-overcall
²take-out

Again the opponents are making things awkward, but with twelve points opposite an opening hand what action should we take?

A (1)

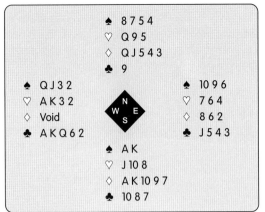

```
                    ♠ 8 7 5 4
                    ♡ Q 9 5
                    ◇ Q J 5 4 3
                    ♣ 9
♠ Q J 3 2                            ♠ 10 9 6
♡ A K 3 2          N                 ♡ 7 6 4
◇ Void          W     E              ◇ 8 6 2
♣ A K Q 6 2        S                 ♣ J 5 4 3
                    ♠ A K
                    ♡ J 10 8
                    ◇ A K 10 9 7
                    ♣ 10 8 7
```

Not a very nice hand, but partner's doubles are most definitely take-out. With 5-5 in the majors he would probably have made a Michaels Cue-Bid so he should hold at least four clubs and that is the suit we should bid. As you can see, we can very nearly make 5♣ whereas the opponents can make 4◇, losing only one club and two hearts.

(2)

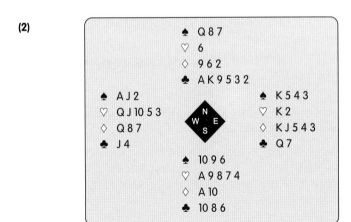

```
                    ♠ Q 8 7
                    ♡ 6
                    ◇ 9 6 2
                    ♣ A K 9 5 3 2
♠ A J 2                              ♠ K 5 4 3
♡ Q J 10 5 3       N                 ♡ K 2
◇ Q 8 7         W     E              ◇ K J 5 4 3
♣ J 4              S                 ♣ Q 7
                    ♠ 10 9 6
                    ♡ A 9 8 7 4
                    ◇ A 10
                    ♣ 10 8 6
```

It can be difficult to stop bidding when we think it is 'our' hand, but here we have a relative misfit. At unfavourable vulnerability, playing at the four level in an unknown fit is too risky; it is best to let them struggle in 4♣.

But don't rush in with a double. Just because we have the majority of the points does not guarantee that this contract is going down; look at our club holding – trumps appear to be breaking well and we have no aces, always a bad omen for defence. Accept that the opponents have bid well and pass.

Q

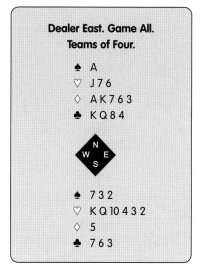

Dealer East. Game All.
Teams of Four.

♠ A
♡ J 7 6
♢ A K 7 6 3
♣ K Q 8 4

♠ 7 3 2
♡ K Q 10 4 3 2
♢ 5
♣ 7 6 3

South	West	North	East
			4♠
Pass	Pass	Double	Pass
5♡	All Pass		

West leads the ♡A and another heart, both defenders following.

It seems that South has made the right bid and 5♡ would have been easy had the defence not drawn two of dummy's trumps.

As it is, we are a trick short: five trumps, two diamonds, one club, one spade, one ruff add up to only ten tricks.

Where will the eleventh come from – diamonds, clubs, or …?

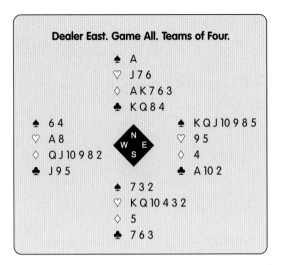

Dealer East. Game All. Teams of Four.

```
               ♠ A
               ♡ J 7 6
               ◇ A K 7 6 3
               ♣ K Q 8 4
♠ 6 4                           ♠ K Q J 10 9 8 5
♡ A 8              N            ♡ 9 5
◇ Q J 10 9 8 2   W   E          ◇ 4
♣ J 9 5            S            ♣ A 10 2
               ♠ 7 3 2
               ♡ K Q 10 4 3 2
               ◇ 5
               ♣ 7 6 3
```

South	West	North	East
			4♠
Pass	Pass	Double	Pass
5♡	All Pass		

West leads the ♡A and another heart, both defenders following.

'This hand looks ripe for a squeeze' will be many experts' first thoughts, but really it is rather more simple: the only chances are a 4-2 diamond break or a 3-3 club break (surely East has the ace of clubs).

Any squeeze chance will quickly evaporate when after winning the ace of clubs the defence return a club to break up the necessary communications. Thus it is important to concentrate on diamonds and clubs, but notice that to test clubs without losing a second trick we will have to discard one from hand on the king of diamonds.

So cash the ace and king of diamonds throwing a club, but East discards too, and our only chance now is in clubs, but we should lead up to the ♣KQ just in case West holds the ace. A diamond ruff to get back to hand and a small club to the king and ace (though ducking would be better technique it does not help on this deal). As expected, East returns a spade, but we ruff in dummy, cash the queen of clubs and ruff a club. The suit does indeed break 3-3 and we have eleven tricks with the spade ruff in dummy; (the other spade goes on the thirteenth club).

Well bid, +650 instead of just +200 from 4♠ doubled one off.

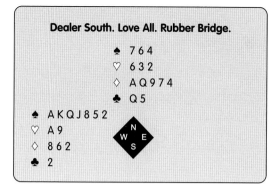

Dealer South. Love All. Rubber Bridge.

```
                        ♠ 7 6 4
                        ♡ 6 3 2
                        ◇ A Q 9 7 4
                        ♣ Q 5
       ♠ A K Q J 8 5 2
       ♡ A 9              N
       ◇ 8 6 2         W     E
       ♣ 2                S
```

South	West	North	East
4♡	4♠	5♡	All Pass

West leads the ♣2 which is taken by dummy's ♣Q;
there follows a trump to the king.

A quick auction, but can we take three tricks?

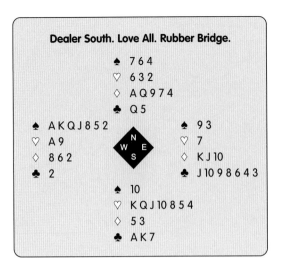

Dealer South. Love All. Rubber Bridge.

	North
♠	7 6 4
♡	6 3 2
◇	A Q 9 7 4
♣	Q 5

West		East
♠ A K Q J 8 5 2		♠ 9 3
♡ A 9		♡ 7
◇ 8 6 2		◇ K J 10
♣ 2		♣ J 10 9 8 6 4 3

	South
♠	10
♡	K Q J 10 8 5 4
◇	5 3
♣	A K 7

South	West	North	East
4♡	4♠	5♡	All Pass

West leads the ♣2 which is taken by dummy's ♣Q;
there follows a trump to the king.

This, I am sorry to say, was a trick question, enticing you to underlead the ♠AKQJ in order to get your partner in to lead a club. And this is exactly what happened at the table, with South being rather happy to make his singleton ten of spades and with it eleven tricks! Partner was not impressed, especially with eleven tricks available in spades for East-West.

Let us think about the position at trick two. Declarer rates to hold something like ♡KQJxxxx and (from the first trick) ♣AKx; that leaves one spade and two diamonds – with two spades declarer would have tried to get rid of one by taking the diamond finesse. But, if he held the king of diamonds, would he not also play on diamonds, trying to throw the spade on a third diamond?

Lead spades from the top and eventually partner will make a diamond trick. Taking the risk of underleading a powerful suit is most gratifying when it pays off, but can it really be worth the embarrassment when it fails?

Q

Dealer South. Love All.
Rubber Bridge.

♠ A J 10 8 3
♡ Q 4 2
◇ A 6
♣ 4 3 2

♠ 4
♡ A K J 10 5
◇ K Q 7
♣ A K 6 5

South	West	North	East
1♡	Pass	1♠	Pass
3♣	Pass	4♡	Pass
4NT¹	Pass	5♡	Pass
5NT¹	Pass	6♣	Pass
6♡	All Pass		

¹standard Blackwood for aces then kings; 5♡ = two aces, 6♣ = no kings

West leads the ♡9.

South seemed a little stuck after the two-ace response. Knowing that she might have a grand slam on, she bid another Blackwood and eventually decided to play safe.

She was rather happier when she saw dummy, quite content to be in the right place with eleven tricks on top and plenty of scope for a twelfth.

A ruff in dummy seems the obvious plan; the problem is how best to achieve this?

Dealer South. Love All. Rubber Bridge.

```
                  ♠ A J 10 8 3
                  ♡ Q 4 2
                  ◇ A 6
                  ♣ 4 3 2
     ♠ Q 5 2                      ♠ K 9 7 6
     ♡ 9 8            N           ♡ 7 6 3
     ◇ J 9 8 5 4 2  W   E         ◇ 10 3
     ♣ Q 9            S           ♣ J 10 8 7
                  ♠ 4
                  ♡ A K J 10 5
                  ◇ K Q 7
                  ♣ A K 6 5
```

South	West	North	East
1♡	Pass	1♠	Pass
3♣	Pass	4♡	Pass
4NT¹	Pass	5♡	Pass
5NT¹	Pass	6♣	Pass
6♡	All Pass		

¹standard Blackwood for aces then kings; 5♡ = two aces, 6♣ = no kings

West leads the ♡9.

Our declarer won the lead in hand with the ten and played three rounds of diamonds throwing a club from dummy. If clubs were 3-3, she might even make an overtrick… Unfortunately, East ruffed the third diamond and returned a trump. Not so nice now, for the clubs failed to break and South was left with a club loser in the endgame – one down.

South was unlucky, but more care would have been rewarded. We do not need overtricks at Rubber Bridge, so we can happily give away a club trick, planning to ruff the fourth club high in dummy.

Win the lead in hand and play the ace of clubs, cross to dummy with the ace of spades and lead a second club (just in case East has a singleton). Win the king of clubs and play a third club, which East wins, but he has no winning options. He tries the ten of diamonds but we win in hand with the king and play a fourth club, ruffing with the queen of hearts. Now draw the trumps and cash the winners – twelve tricks and our 500 bonus in the bank.

Dealer South. North-South Game.

```
                    ♠ A 7
                    ♡ K Q
                    ◊ 9 4 2
                    ♣ K Q 8 6 5 2
    ♠ K J 9 6
    ♡ 8 7 6 4              N
    ◊ A 10 7          W         E
    ♣ A 9                 S
```

South	West	North	East
1◊	Double	Redouble	2♡¹
2♠	Pass	3♣	Pass
3◊	Pass	5◊	Pass
Pass	Double	All Pass	

¹pre-emptive with five hearts

West leads the ♡7 and declarer overtakes dummy's ♡Q
with the ♡A (partner plays the ♡2); he then plays the ♣J.

A dubious double, but you were surprised at North-South's reluctance to
bid no-trumps and thus placed partner with a card or two in hearts. But
partner rates to hold only one or two points and exactly five hearts (his card
at trick one reaffirms this), so we should not rely on him for anything. Too
late now! South appears to be 4-2-6-1 shape (he must have two hearts if
partner has five) for his bidding.

So given that the jack is a singleton, what can you do to scuttle the
contract?

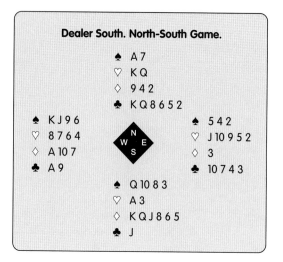

Dealer South. North-South Game.

	♠ A 7	
	♡ K Q	
	◊ 9 4 2	
	♣ K Q 8 6 5 2	
♠ K J 9 6		♠ 5 4 2
♡ 8 7 6 4		♡ J 10 9 5 2
◊ A 10 7		◊ 3
♣ A 9		♣ 10 7 4 3
	♠ Q 10 8 3	
	♡ A 3	
	◊ K Q J 8 6 5	
	♣ J	

South	West	North	East
1◊	Double	Redouble	2♡¹
2♠	Pass	3♣	Pass
3◊	Pass	5◊	Pass
Pass	Double	All Pass	

¹pre-emptive with five hearts

West leads the ♡7 and declarer overtakes dummy's ♡Q with the ♡A (partner plays the ♡2); he then plays the ♣J.

Ducking is no good. Declarer switches to trumps which you win and play a heart, but declarer can simply ruff a club (felling your ace), draw trumps, re-enter dummy with the ace of spades and cash clubs, making with an overtrick!

So we win the ace of clubs and switch to a heart to knock out an entry to dummy. Declarer ruffs a club to establish the suit and plays trumps. We win the second round (or the first), but now what?

Our only hope is to knock out declarer's entry to dummy before he can draw our trumps but how do we do that? Exit with the king of spades! Declarer has to win, but cannot play clubs because we can ruff. So he follows with the queen of spades and a spade ruff, but he still has to give up one trick, to the ten of diamonds or the jack of spades.

A great play, and well timed. If we play the king of spades after the ace of clubs, it is too early, for declarer will see that there is no need to establish clubs and play for a spade ruff instead – the fourth spade going on the king of clubs – thus making eleven tricks.

Bernard Magee's Bridge Quiz Book

Q

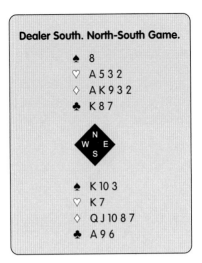

Dealer South. North-South Game.

- ♠ 8
- ♡ A 5 3 2
- ◇ A K 9 3 2
- ♣ K 8 7

- ♠ K 10 3
- ♡ K 7
- ◇ Q J 10 8 7
- ♣ A 9 6

South	West	North	East
1◇	3♣	4♠[1]	Pass
5♣[2]	Pass	6◇	All Pass

[1] slam try in diamonds
[2] cue-bid; not good enough to accept the slam try, but willing to co-operate

West leads the ◇6.

Once again, the opponents have succeeded in randomising the auction and it seems we might have stretched just too far. Can we justify the optimistic slam?

A

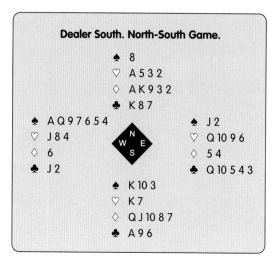

Dealer South. North-South Game.

```
              ♠ 8
              ♡ A 5 3 2
              ◊ A K 9 3 2
              ♣ K 8 7
♠ A Q 9 7 6 5 4          ♠ J 2
♡ J 8 4          N          ♡ Q 10 9 6
◊ 6          W     E          ◊ 5 4
♣ J 2          S          ♣ Q 10 5 4 3
              ♠ K 10 3
              ♡ K 7
              ◊ Q J 10 8 7
              ♣ A 9 6
```

South	West	North	East
1◊	3♠	4♠¹	Pass
5♣²	Pass	6◊	All Pass

¹slam try in diamonds
²cue bid; not good enough to accept the slam try, but willing to co-operate

West leads the ◊6.

We have two possible losers – one in spades and one in clubs – and have to aim to establish a trick in spades to discard the club loser. Our chances are poor, especially as on the bidding East is highly unlikely to hold the ace of spades, but there does seem to be a chance of endplaying West with the aid of a partial elimination. We require West to have no more than two clubs and to hold the ace of spades and at least one other honour in the suit.

Win the ace of diamonds, cash the king and ace of hearts and follow with a heart ruff. Continue with another diamond (drawing trumps) and a second heart ruff. Now cash the ace and king of clubs and hopefully West is down to only spades.

We now play a spade from dummy, ready to insert the ten if East plays low, thereby forcing West to win and lead away from his ace. However, East is alert to the danger and inserts the jack, but to no avail, for we can cover with the king and although West wins his ace he now has to lead away from his queen – twelve tricks.

Dealer North. Game All.
Teams of Four.

> ♠ Q J 7 2
> ♡ A K 5 4
> ◇ Q 10 3
> ♣ 7 4

> ♠ A K 9 8 6 3
> ♡ Q 9
> ◇ K 7
> ♣ K 9 6

South	West	North	East
		1◇[1]	Pass
1♠	3♣[2]	3♠	Pass
4♣	Double	4♡	Pass
4NT[3]	Pass	5◇[3]	Pass
5♠	All Pass		

[1] better minor (five-card majors, strong no-trump)
[2] intermediate, 10–15 points, six-card suit
[3] Blackwood, the 5◇ response showing one ace

West leads the ♡8.

It looks as though we might have gone too far. Was 4NT too optimistic? After all West had shown an intermediate hand and partner would have bid 3♠ on nearly any hand with four-card support.

How can we avoid three losers in the minor suits?

A

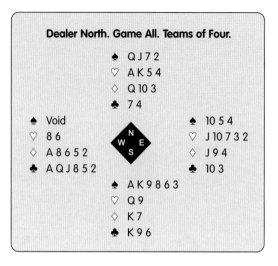

Dealer North. Game All. Teams of Four.

	♠ Q J 7 2	
	♡ A K 5 4	
	◇ Q 10 3	
	♣ 7 4	

♠ Void   ♠ 10 5 4
♡ 8 6   ♡ J 10 7 3 2
◇ A 8 6 5 2   ◇ J 9 4
♣ A Q J 8 5 2   ♣ 10 3

♠ A K 9 8 6 3
♡ Q 9
◇ K 7
♣ K 9 6

South	West	North	East
		1◇[1]	Pass
1♠	3♣[2]	3♠	Pass
4♣	Double	4♡	Pass
4NT[3]	Pass	5◇[3]	Pass
5♠	All Pass		

[1]better minor (five-card majors, strong no-trump)
[2]intermediate, 10–15 points, six-card suit
[3]Blackwood, the 5◇ response showing one ace

West leads the ♡8.

From the bidding, West surely holds both aces and thus our lifeline lies in a play called the Morton's Fork Coup. Win the queen of hearts, draw three rounds of trumps, ending in hand and lead a small diamond towards dummy.

If West rises with the ace, he establishes two diamond tricks for us (the king and queen) yielding a second club discard to go with the first from the heart suit. West, of course, cannot profitably attack the club suit from his side, so he is helpless.

If West ducks the diamond lead, we win the queen and cash two more rounds of hearts throwing the king of diamonds. Thus, if he rises, we lose one diamond and one club; and if he ducks we lose just two clubs.

Not a pleasant situation for a defender – on the end of a fork!

Q BRIDGE TRIVIA

1. Whom did Ely Culbertson partner for the majority of the Culbertson-Lenz Match ('The Bridge Battle of the Century')?

2. Who introduced transfers over a 1NT opening?

3. Who was the only player to participate in all sixteen Italian world victories between 1957 and 1975?

4. Which two British players were involved in the 'Buenos Aires Affair'?

5. Whose bidding methods became labelled 'Standard American'?

6. Who devised the Precision system of bidding?

7. Who was the bridge editor of the Guardian from 1955 to 1992 and one of the greatest women bridge players of all time?

8. Which is the odd one out: Stayman, Ripstra, Baron, Brozel or Gerber?

9. Who won the first Omar Sharif World Individual in 1990?

10. Who invented the Blackwood convention?

11. Which pair of twins helped Great Britain to the 1995 World Junior title and which pair of twins helped win the same title in 1989?

12. What are Robertson, Bamberger, Reith and Work?

13. From which country are these players; Bauke Muller, Wubbo de Boer, Piet Jansen, Jan Westerhof, Enri Leufkens, Berry Westra and (npc) Jaap Trouwborst, winners of the 1993 Bermuda Bowl?

14. Which is the odd one out: Culbertson, Jacoby, Kaplan, Kokish, Blackwood, or Rodwell?

15. Which Swede introduced the bidding box?

16. Who put together and funded the Aces teams (US) which won the Bermuda Bowl in 1970 and 1971 among other successes?

17. Who was one of the originators of the Acol system and wrote the book Why you lose at Bridge?

18. Which company sponsored a series of contests for bridge tips?

19. Which Norwegian won the 1996 World Individual and whilst still a junior (under 25) represented his country in the Bermuda Bowl final of 1993?

20. Who is supposed to have been responsible for the introduction of bridge at the Portland Club (London) in 1894 which resulted in the rapid spread of the game throughout England?

A ANSWERS TO BRIDGE TRIVIA

1. His wife, Josephine Culbertson.

2. Oswald Jacoby.

3. Giorgio Belladonna.

4. Terence Reese and Boris Schapiro.

5. Charles Goren.

6. Charles Wei.

7. Rixi Markus.

8. Brozel – the others are conventions which take the precise name of their inventor. Brozel was invented by Bernard Zeller.

9. Zia Mahmood.

10. Easley Blackwood.

11. 1995 – Jason and Justin Hackett; 1989 – Gerald and Stuart Tredinnick.

12. Systems for point counting.

13. The Netherlands.

14. Jacoby (Oswald) – the others have first names beginning with E: Ely, Edgar, Eric, Easley and Eric respectively.

15. Eric Jannersten.

16. Ira Corn.

17. S J Simon.

18. Bols.

19. Geir Helgemo.

20. Lord Brougham.

Chapter 7

Three No-Trumps

The most popular game contract, simply because it requires the least tricks. It is probably too popular at Duplicate bridge, bid by players scrounging for that extra ten points that no-trumps yields. But it is well worth getting some practice, so here is a chapter-full. Here we have a special trivia section on cards and card games in general.

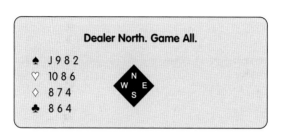

Dealer North. Game All.

♠ J 9 8 2
♡ 10 8 6
♢ 8 7 4
♣ 8 6 4

South	West	North	East
		1♢	Pass
1♠	Pass	3♢	Pass
3NT	All Pass		

An uninspiring hand, but remember we have a fellow conspirator and his hand is probably a lot better than ours. Let us think for him; what would he like us to lead?

A

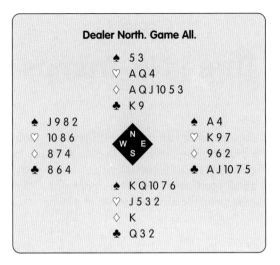

Dealer North. Game All.

```
                  ♠  5 3
                  ♡  A Q 4
                  ◇  A Q J 10 5 3
                  ♣  K 9
   ♠  J 9 8 2                      ♠  A 4
   ♡  10 8 6          N            ♡  K 9 7
   ◇  8 7 4        W     E         ◇  9 6 2
   ♣  8 6 4          S             ♣  A J 10 7 5
                  ♠  K Q 10 7 6
                  ♡  J 5 3 2
                  ◇  K
                  ♣  Q 3 2
```

South	West	North	East
		1◇	Pass
1♠	Pass	3◇	Pass
3NT	All Pass		

To have a reasonable chance of defeating this contract, partner will have to hold ten or eleven points and a long suit. The question is, which suit? The important thing to note is his silence during the auction. Over North's 1◇ opening, East might well have overcalled 1♡ with five hearts, but with five clubs he may have been more circumspect (an overcall at the two-level requires a better hand and a better suit). These inferences should point us in the right direction for our lead.

Lead the six of clubs (Middle, Up, Down from three small cards) following with the eight on the second round. Here, partner wins dummy's king with his ace and returns the suit. Declarer has eight top tricks and tries for a ninth by taking the heart finesse, but partner wins his king and cashes his clubs along with the ace of spades, for two down.

If you swap East's hearts and clubs, there is no doubting that most would overcall 1♡, and with good reason – because it tells partner which suit to lead!

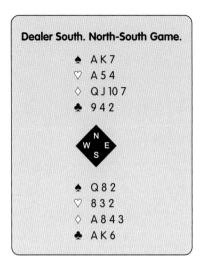

Dealer South. North-South Game.

```
              ♠ A K 7
              ♡ A 5 4
              ◇ Q J 10 7
              ♣ 9 4 2

                   N
                W     E
                   S

              ♠ Q 8 2
              ♡ 8 3 2
              ◇ A 8 4 3
              ♣ A K 6
```

South	West	North	East
1NT¹	Pass	3NT	All Pass

¹weak no-trump 12–14

West leads the ♡J.

Straightforward bidding on what looks like a straightforward hand. If the hearts break 5-2 and West also holds the king of diamonds, we will be one down, otherwise we are home and dry. Can things really be that easy?

A

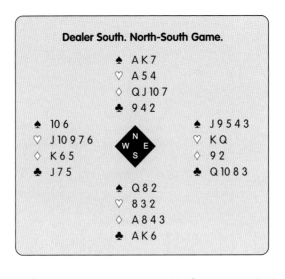

Dealer South. North-South Game.

```
                    ♠ A K 7
                    ♡ A 5 4
                    ◇ Q J 10 7
                    ♣ 9 4 2
        ♠ 10 6                      ♠ J 9 5 4 3
        ♡ J 10 9 7 6    N           ♡ K Q
        ◇ K 6 5      W     E        ◇ 9 2
        ♣ J 7 5         S           ♣ Q 10 8 3
                    ♠ Q 8 2
                    ♡ 8 3 2
                    ◇ A 8 4 3
                    ♣ A K 6
```

South	West	North	East
1NT[1]	Pass	3NT	All Pass

[1] weak no-trump 12–14

West leads the ♡J.

Things are actually slightly easier than they seem! The analysis overleaf was right up to a point, but it overlooked the chance of the heart suit being blocked. If West has led away from ♡J109 (without the king) then, when the suit splits 5-2, his partner will hold ♡KQ bare, so we can take the first heart trick and leave the suit blocked. Now, when we take the diamond finesse, West wins but the defence can only take one heart trick and we can claim nine tricks.

Of course, if the suit was not blocked we were destined for one down if West held the protected king of diamonds, whether we held up in hearts or not because there would be nothing we could do to stop him cashing his winners.

But even this line overlooks one extra chance – a singleton queen of hearts with East.

To cover both cases, it is correct to duck hearts until the defence cannot lead any more. In the above case, we duck twice and then East has to switch, because he is out of hearts. If East had held the singleton queen, he would have been forced to switch at trick two.

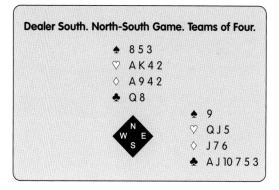

Dealer South. North-South Game. Teams of Four.

    ♠ 8 5 3
    ♡ A K 4 2
    ◇ A 9 4 2
    ♣ Q 8

    ♠ 9
    ♡ Q J 5
    ◇ J 7 6
    ♣ A J 10 7 5 3

South	West	North	East
1NT	2♠	3♠[1]	Pass
3NT	All Pass		

[1] showing four hearts and no spade stopper

West leads the ♠K followed by the ♠J on which
we throw a club while South wins with the ♠A.

Dummy has thirteen points, we hold nine and partner has at least six; that leaves only twelve points, which must be in South's hand (12–14). So, knowing that partner holds no high card outside spades, can we still take this contract down?

A

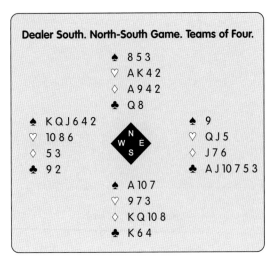

Dealer South. North-South Game. Teams of Four.

	♠ 8 5 3	
	♡ A K 4 2	
	◊ A 9 4 2	
	♣ Q 8	
♠ K Q J 6 4 2		♠ 9
♡ 10 8 6		♡ Q J 5
◊ 5 3		◊ J 7 6
♣ 9 2		♣ A J 10 7 5 3
	♠ A 10 7	
	♡ 9 7 3	
	◊ K Q 10 8	
	♣ K 6 4	

South	West	North	East
1NT	2♠	3♠[1]	Pass
3NT	All Pass		

[1]showing four hearts and no spade stopper

West leads the ♠K followed by the ♠J on which
we throw a club while South wins with the ♠A.

West is unlikely to have a second suit so declarer is set to make four diamond tricks, together with one club, one spade and two hearts which makes eight. A third heart winner (after giving up a trick in the suit) would take his tally up to nine. If we win the defence's heart trick we can do declarer no harm, so our only hope is to create a heart entry for partner by unblocking our high hearts beneath the ace, king in dummy – if partner holds the ten of hearts, he will then be able to take the third round of hearts and with it his spade winners.

South leads a heart which West makes sure to cover, North has to win, and we throw the queen underneath the ace. Declarer crosses back to hand and leads another heart. Once again West covers South's card and North has to win with the king, allowing us to throw the jack. Now in order to establish his third heart trick declarer has to let West gain the lead and thus lose four more spade tricks as well as the ace of clubs – three down (or perhaps just two down if declarer cashes his diamonds).

Bernard Magee's Bridge Quiz Book

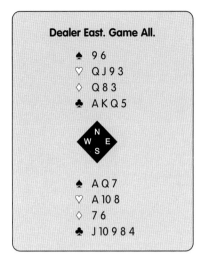

Dealer East. Game All.

```
          ♠ 9 6
          ♡ Q J 9 3
          ◇ Q 8 3
          ♣ A K Q 5

              N
          W       E
              S

          ♠ A Q 7
          ♡ A 10 8
          ◇ 7 6
          ♣ J 10 9 8 4
```

South	West	North	East
			Pass
Pass	1♠	Double	2♠
2NT	Pass	3NT	All Pass

West leads the ♠4 to East's ♠J.

A slightly awkward bidding sequence here but it hasn't worked out too badly. However, we are one trick short. It will be easy enough to create a ninth, but what about diamonds?

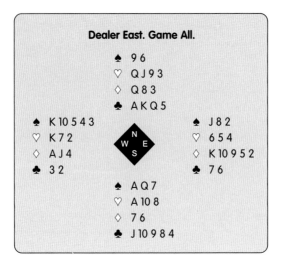

Dealer East. Game All.

	♠ 9 6
	♡ Q J 9 3
	◇ Q 8 3
	♣ A K Q 5

♠ K 10 5 4 3   ♠ J 8 2
♡ K 7 2   ♡ 6 5 4
◇ A J 4   ◇ K 10 9 5 2
♣ 3 2   ♣ 7 6

            ♠ A Q 7
            ♡ A 10 8
            ◇ 7 6
            ♣ J 10 9 8 4

South	West	North	East
			Pass
Pass	1♠	Double	2♠
2NT	Pass	3NT	All Pass

West leads the ♠4 to East's ♠J.

The most obvious play is to win the queen of spades, cross to dummy in clubs and finesse in hearts. But if West wins this trick, he will know that you still have the spades stopped (East would have played the ace on the first round if he had it) and he will see his only chance is to switch to diamonds and the defence will take their six tricks.

How can we put the defence off this line?

Our best chance is to try a little deceptive play. Win the first trick with the *ace* of spades and then cross to dummy and take the heart finesse. Now things seem very clear to West: his side have four more spades to cash so he leads to his partner's queen of spades and ... we run for home with five clubs, three hearts and two spades.

West might have played the king of spades, under which East could throw the queen if he had it, but if we disbelieve declarer all the time we are going to make life very difficult for ourselves.

Dealer South. Love All.

South	West	North	East
3NT	Double	?	

Your partner's 3NT was 'gambling', showing a long and solid minor (seven or more cards) and nothing else. It gambles on the partner, North in this instance, holding two more tricks to make up the necessary nine.

What would you respond on the following hands?

(1)
- ♠ A 5 4
- ♡ A 8 4 2
- ◇ 5 4 3 2
- ♣ 6 4

(2)
- ♠ 6 5 3 2
- ♡ A
- ◇ 10 6 4 3
- ♣ 10 8 4 2

(3)
- ♠ A 5 4 3
- ♡ 5
- ◇ A 9 6 4 2
- ♣ 10 8 4

(4)
- ♠ K 5 4
- ♡ K 8 4 2
- ◇ 5 4 3 2
- ♣ 6 4

(5)
- ♠ A K 5 4 3
- ♡ 8 4 2
- ◇ A 6 5 4 2
- ♣ Void

A Partner will hold something like:

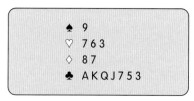

```
♠ 9
♡ 7 6 3
◇ 8 7
♣ A K Q J 7 5 3
```

When a call can be one of two suits, as in this case either minor, then our responses are often for 'correction'. This means that, if we are unsure of which minor partner holds, we bid the lower suit (clubs) and if he holds clubs, he will pass, but with diamonds he will correct the contract by bidding diamonds.

On hands (3) and (5), we know which suit partner holds because we hold a top honour in the other minor, but on the others, we are in the dark until the bidding continues.

(1) Pass – A worthwhile gamble. We should have nine tricks on top and the only way we can go down is if our opponents lead diamonds and one of them has a five-card suit.

(2) 5♣ – Get in the way of the opponents. From our hand, it looks as though they may well make a slam, but they will most definitely make game. We should only go one or two off in 5♣ doubled, which will be a good score: –300 against –420 or –450. The situation is the same whether partner holds clubs or diamonds and with the latter, he will bid 5◇.

(3) 5♣ – This time we hope to make the game: two aces, seven trumps and hopefully two heart ruffs. Passing 3NT is risky because a heart lead will most likely net five or six tricks for the defence (compare this with (1), where we held four cards in the danger suit and thus the risk was much less).

(4) 4♣ – A weak hand and probably not a fit. Let partner play in his suit at the four level.

(5) 4♣ – This hand looks quite nice, but even if the opponents fail to lead hearts against 3NT, we have no way to get to partner's hand. Again we must allow partner to play in four of his suit, hoping to make our three top tricks and seven trumps.

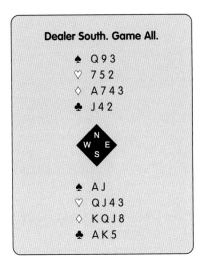

Dealer South. Game All.

♠ Q 9 3
♡ 7 5 2
◇ A 7 4 3
♣ J 4 2

N
W   E
S

♠ A J
♡ Q J 4 3
◇ K Q J 8
♣ A K 5

South	West	North	East
2NT	Pass	3NT	All Pass

West leads the ♠2.

A quick auction and a quick lead – time to think. Seven top tricks, an extra trick on the lead makes eight, but where is the ninth coming from?

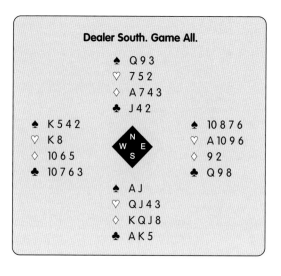

Dealer South. Game All.

```
                    ♠ Q 9 3
                    ♡ 7 5 2
                    ◇ A 7 4 3
                    ♣ J 4 2
    ♠ K 5 4 2                      ♠ 10 8 7 6
    ♡ K 8          N              ♡ A 10 9 6
    ◇ 10 6 5     W   E            ◇ 9 2
    ♣ 10 7 6 3     S              ♣ Q 9 8
                    ♠ A J
                    ♡ Q J 4 3
                    ◇ K Q J 8
                    ♣ A K 5
```

South	West	North	East
2NT	Pass	3NT	All Pass

West leads the ♠2.

Hearts seem to be the only suit offering good chances of extending our trick tally. If the defenders lead clubs, we might pick up one there, but that seems unlikely. It looks as though we will need spades 4-4 and so the two of spades lead (usually fourth highest) is a pleasing sight.

How best to play the hearts? This is why we needed to think before playing from dummy to trick one. Ideally, we would like to lead up to the queen, jack of hearts twice, so that we can make an extra trick whenever East holds both honours or when the defenders hold one each. But how many entries do we have? Only one it seems (ace of diamonds), but of course, if West has led away from the king of spades we can create another by rising with the queen. This cannot really cost and here it certainly gains.

So, win trick one with the queen of spades and lead a heart to the queen and king. Now win the spade return, cross to dummy with the ace of diamonds and lead another heart. East wins, so we can play low, and our heart trick is established. Now we cross our fingers as East-West cash their remaining spades. Lo and behold, the spades do break 4-4 and we have our nine tricks for the contract.

Q

Dealer South. East-West Game.

```
              ♠ K Q 4
              ♡ A 9 6 3
              ◇ Q J 6
              ♣ 4 3 2
  ♠ 7 2              N
  ♡ J 10 5 4     W     E
  ◇ K 5 4           S
  ♣ A K Q 10
```

South	West	North	East
1NT¹	Pass	2♣	Pass
2♠	Pass	3NT	All Pass

¹weak no-trump (12–14)

West leads the ♣A, ♣Q, ♣K and a fourth club, everybody following to
the first three rounds; on the fourth, the ◇J is thrown by dummy,
the ◇9 by partner and the ◇2 by declarer.

The weak no-trump opening means that partner can have a maximum of
three points, but he actually turned up with the jack of clubs so that leaves
just two more. He might hold the jack of spades or the queen of hearts, but
he cannot hold the ace of diamonds. What do you lead, and secondly, what
will you discard if South can run four spade tricks?

A

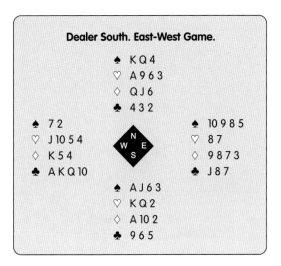

Dealer South. East-West Game.

```
                    ♠ K Q 4
                    ♡ A 9 6 3
                    ◇ Q J 6
                    ♣ 4 3 2
   ♠ 7 2                          ♠ 10 9 8 5
   ♡ J 10 5 4          N          ♡ 8 7
   ◇ K 5 4         W     E        ◇ 9 8 7 3
   ♣ A K Q 10         S           ♣ J 8 7
                    ♠ A J 6 3
                    ♡ K Q 2
                    ◇ A 10 2
                    ♣ 9 6 5
```

South	West	North	East
1NT[1]	Pass	2♣	Pass
2♠	Pass	3NT	All Pass

[1]weak no-trump (12–14)

West leads the ♣A, ♣Q, ♣K and a fourth club, everybody following to
the first three rounds; on the fourth, the ◇J is thrown by dummy,
the ◇9 by partner and the ◇2 by declarer.

All we want to do at this stage of the defence is to get off lead and a spade
is clearly our safest exit. The most important thing when defending this
type of hand is to think ahead. What will we discard on four spades? We
will be in trouble because we want to keep four hearts and two diamonds,
but we can only keep five cards. What should we discard? Two low
diamonds, nice and smoothly.

Declarer will throw the queen of diamonds on the fourth spade and
then cash three top hearts. He knows that we hold the last heart and thus
only one diamond, but if we did not squirm, he will assume it is a small
diamond and finesse East for the king – two down. Of course if he guesses
we hold the king of diamonds he can simply cash the ace and ten for the
last two tricks.

When being squeezed, you should never assume that declarer knows
what is happening and be careful not to give anything away by your
expression.

Q

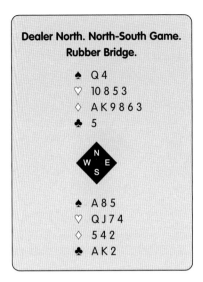

Dealer North. North-South Game.
Rubber Bridge.

    ♠ Q 4
    ♡ 10 8 5 3
    ◊ A K 9 8 6 3
    ♣ 5

              N
          W   E
              S

    ♠ A 8 5
    ♡ Q J 7 4
    ◊ 5 4 2
    ♣ A K 2

South	West	North	East
		3◊	Pass
3NT	All Pass		

West leads the ♠3 and dummy's ♠Q holds the trick.

At unfavourable vulnerability South expected his partner's pre-empt to be reasonable and so gambled on 3NT. Only six diamonds and four hearts! However, North has the top two diamonds and the lead has given us an unexpected bonus. Can we take advantage?

A

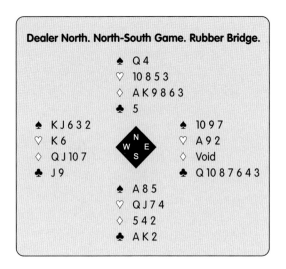

Dealer North. North-South Game. Rubber Bridge.

```
                    ♠ Q 4
                    ♡ 10 8 5 3
                    ◇ A K 9 8 6 3
                    ♣ 5
  ♠ K J 6 3 2              ♠ 10 9 7
  ♡ K 6          N         ♡ A 9 2
  ◇ Q J 10 7   W   E       ◇ Void
  ♣ J 9          S         ♣ Q 10 8 7 6 4 3
                    ♠ A 8 5
                    ♡ Q J 7 4
                    ◇ 5 4 2
                    ♣ A K 2
```

South	West	North	East
		3◇	Pass
3NT	All Pass		

West leads the ♠3 and dummy's ♠Q holds the trick.

Whenever a contract looks easy, think again. What can go wrong? A 4-0 diamond split is the only thing that can endanger this contract. If East holds the four diamonds, there is little we can do, but if West holds them, we can take a double finesse and thus lose only one trick in the suit. Entries are short so the best way to tackle the suit is to lose our trick first.

Win the queen of spades and lead the nine of diamonds. West wins and returns a spade which we win in hand. Now West rises with the jack when we lead a diamond so we win the ace and have to return to hand with a club, remembering to cash both the ace and king of clubs while we are there. Then the last diamond picks up the suit, netting nine tricks.

                     Bernard Magee's Bridge Quiz Book

Q

```
                    Dealer East. Game All.
                         ♠  A
                         ♡  K J 10 7 3
                         ◇  A 7 5
                         ♣  A K Q J
```

```
                         ♠  K 8 5 2
                         ♡  9 8 6
                         ◇  J 10 9 4
                         ♣  10 4
```

South	West	North	East
			1♠
Pass	Pass	Double	Pass
2◇	Pass	2♠	Pass
2NT	Pass	3♠	Pass
3NT	All Pass		

West leads the ♠9.

Not an easy one to bid. An immediate 2♠ would have shown a two suiter (Michaels Cue-Bid) rather than a very powerful hand, so North had to start with a double. Perhaps over 2NT, North should bid 3♡, which is surely forcing but perhaps promises a better suit? Do you have a secure agreement with your partner over this one?

Anyway, although we have not found the best contract, we still have plenty of chances to succeed where we are, but what are the best chances?

How should we play?

A

Dealer East. Game All.

```
                  ♠ A
                  ♡ K J 10 7 3
                  ◇ A 7 5
                  ♣ A K Q J
     ♠ 9 7 4              ♠ Q J 10 6 3
     ♡ Q 5 2         N    ♡ A 4
     ◇ 6 3 2      W     E ◇ K Q 8
     ♣ 9 8 5 2       S    ♣ 7 6 3
                  ♠ K 8 5 2
                  ♡ 9 8 6
                  ◇ J 10 9 4
                  ♣ 10 4
```

South	West	North	East
			1♠
Pass	Pass	Double	Pass
2◇	Pass	2♠	Pass
2NT	Pass	3♠	Pass
3NT	All Pass		

West leads the ♠9.

The main danger in 3NT is the spade suit. We know where most of the points are; East's opening bid suggests that West is unlikely to have more than a queen.

If East holds all the cards, we are going down. What card can we give West so that we might succeed?

A diamond is no good, so how about the queen of hearts? How can this help? Well, if we can establish our hearts whilst giving the lead away to East first then we should be able to make sure that West holds no more spades when he wins the second heart.

To force East to win the first trick, we play the king of hearts. East wins his ace and plays the queen of spades, which we duck and win the next round. Now when we lose a heart to West's queen he has no spades to lead and we are able to win any switch and claim our ten tricks.

Note that, because East has a doubleton heart, it does him no good to duck the king because he will have to win the next round anyway.

Bernard Magee's Bridge Quiz Book

Q BRIDGE TRIVIA

1. Court Cards and Spot Cards – which four cards in the pack do not fall into either of these categories?

2. Who wrote *The Queen of Spades?*

3. How many cards are there in a Piquet pack?

4. Of what are Clock, The Demon, Oracle, Sir Tommy and Rosamund's Bower examples?

5. Which court cards show only one eye on each face?

6. What are Lowball, Spit, Hold 'em and Stud?

7. What are the French, British and American names for the game of Twenty-One?

8. What is the basic aim in a game of Hearts?

9. Which cards are required for a 'Double Bezique' ?

10. In which countries are the traditional suits Acorns, Leaves, Hearts and Bells?

11. From which country did the game of Canasta originate?

12. Which is the odd one out: Maria, Peter, Jack or Joan?

13. Playing Klaberjass or Belote, what is the highest card in the trump suit?

14. Which card was key in the game of Nain Jaune (Yellow Dwarf) and which was key in Pope Joan?

15. A Tarot pack usually consists of 78 cards – four suits of fourteen cards, twenty-one trumps and what other card?

16. What is a 'Prial' ?

17. Which of the suits of court cards does not have each member facing the same way?

18. What is the highest hand in three-card Brag?

19. Which is the odd one out: 21, 31, 41, 51, 66 or 99?

20. What game can be Chinese, German, Dutch, Norwegian, Russian, Scotch and Welsh?

A   ANSWERS TO BRIDGE TRIVIA

1. The four aces.

2. Alexander Pushkin.

3. Thirty-two.

4. Games of Patience (or Solitaire).

5. King of diamonds, jack of spades and jack of hearts.

6. Forms of Poker.

7. Vingt-et-Un (Fr), Pontoon (GB), and Blackjack (US).

8. To lose tricks (especially those with hearts in).

9. The two queens of spades and the two jacks of diamonds.

10. Germany and Switzerland.

11. Uruguay.

12. Joan – the others may be prefixed by black to give the name of a card game.

13. The jack.

14. Seven of diamonds in Yellow Dwarf; and nine of diamonds in Pope Joan.

15. The Fool.

16. A triplet; three cards of the same rank (a shortening of 'pair royale').

17. Clubs – the jack faces right and the king and queen face left (as we look).

18. Three threes.

19. 41 – the others are all card games!

20. Whist.

Chapter 8

Conventions

There is a truly amazing number of conventions, some more popular than others! The problems in this section deal with very few, but at least it gives you a chance to see some different types of bidding sequence. It is also important to try to understand the auction in order to help your defence to some of the contracts. The trivia section quizzes your knowledge of conventions in general.

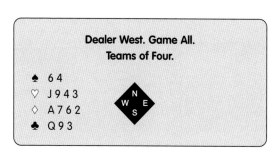

Dealer West. Game All.
Teams of Four.

♠ 6 4
♡ J 9 4 3
◇ A 7 6 2
♣ Q 9 3

South	West	North	East
	Pass	1♡	Pass
1♠	Pass	4♣¹	Pass
5♣²	Pass	5♡²	Pass
5♠	All Pass		

¹splinter, showing short clubs with four-card spade support
²first-round control

One of the disadvantages of accurate systems is that they make things easier for the defenders. Can we make use of the above auction to punish the opponents for stretching in search of slam?

What should we lead?

A

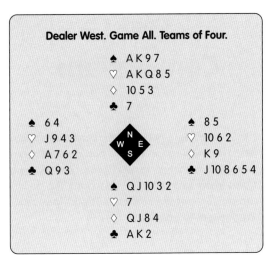

Dealer West. Game All. Teams of Four.

♠ A K 9 7
♡ A K Q 8 5
♢ 10 5 3
♣ 7

♠ 6 4
♡ J 9 4 3
♢ A 7 6 2
♣ Q 9 3

♠ 8 5
♡ 10 6 2
♢ K 9
♣ J 10 8 6 5 4

♠ Q J 10 3 2
♡ 7
♢ Q J 8 4
♣ A K 2

South	West	North	East
	Pass	1♡	Pass
1♠	Pass	4♣[1]	Pass
5♣[2]	Pass	5♡[2]	Pass
5♠	All Pass		

[1]splinter, showing short clubs with four-card spade support
[2]first-round control

Over 4♣, South would have tried to cue-bid in diamonds if he had a control and again over 5♣ North had the chance to cue-bid diamonds, but failed. They were certainly both bidding positively, so, it seems that, except for the diamond suit, this contract should be easy.

So we pull out the ace of diamonds, but hold on, have we not just decided that they are without the ace *and* king of diamonds? Surely we do best to underlead our ace in the hope that partner has a doubleton king (or KJ10), and this then gives us the hope of defeating the contract. If North or South turns up with the king of diamonds anyway, so be it, but they would probably make 5♠ anyway and quite possibly 6♣.

Here the two of diamonds works perfectly: partner wins the king and returns the suit to our ace and finally the third diamond is ruffed. 5♠ – 1.

Sometimes we underlead an ace with a vain hope against a solidly-bid contract, but here we are using the science of the auction and are quite justified.

Q

Dealer South. Game All.

♠ K Q J 7 4
♡ 10 4 2
◇ 9 2
♣ K 10 5

♠ A 10 8 6 2
♡ Q J 7
◇ A Q
♣ A J 8

South	West	North	East
1♠	Double	2NT¹	Pass
3♣²	Pass	3♠	Pass
4◇²	Pass	4♠	All Pass

¹limit raise to 3♠ (10–12 points); 3♠ would show a weaker hand
²3♣ is a game-try, but might show a better hand; when South bids on after North's sign-off, the inference is that both 3♣ and 4◇ are cue-bids

West leads the ♡K, ♡A and another heart, all following.

North has an interesting bid over 1♠ doubled, some players might even leap to 4♠, but he decided that he would normally have responded 3♠ to 1♠ and hence that 2NT was the correct response. Over South's game try, North should probably bid game with help in clubs and an extra spade, but as it turns out, he was rather lucky because South was slam bound and they might have found themselves in an unmakeable 5♠.

Anyway 4♠ was bid eventually, but even that contract is not laydown because the trick-taking potential of the hands is rather damaged by the duplication of shape. We do have some clues though because West doubled South's opening bid, but is that a help or a hindrance?

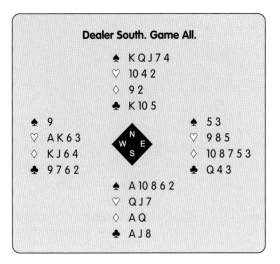

Dealer South. Game All.

```
                    ♠ K Q J 7 4
                    ♡ 10 4 2
                    ◇ 9 2
                    ♣ K 10 5
        ♠ 9                           ♠ 5 3
        ♡ A K 6 3          N          ♡ 9 8 5
        ◇ K J 6 4      W       E      ◇ 10 8 7 5 3
        ♣ 9 7 6 2          S          ♣ Q 4 3
                    ♠ A 10 8 6 2
                    ♡ Q J 7
                    ◇ A Q
                    ♣ A J 8
```

South	West	North	East
1♠	Double	2NT[1]	Pass
3♣[2]	Pass	3♠	Pass
4◇[2]	Pass	4♠	All Pass

[1]limit raise to 3♠ (10–12 points); 3♠ would show a weaker hand
[2]3♣ is a game-try, but might show a better hand; when South bids on after North's sign-off, the inference is that both 3♣ and 4◇ are cue-bids

West leads the ♡K, ♡A and another heart, all following.

A lazy declarer would think the work done when he had placed West with all the outstanding points – after all, there are only thirteen and they are vulnerable and the double was of 1♠ and...

Yes, that declarer would have a lot to say for himself in the post-mortem after he had finessed West for the queen of clubs and lost; one down when the diamond finesse lost as expected.

The bidding in this case is actually a hindrance, for without it our declarer would probably have found the correct 100% play. Draw trumps and play the ace of diamonds followed by the queen of diamonds. Whoever wins their king will be endplayed, forced to concede a ruff and discard in a red suit or to open up the club suit enabling declarer to find the queen harmlessly.

Q

Dealer North. Love All. Duplicate Pairs.

```
                          ♠ Q J 2
                          ♡ K Q 6 2
                          ◇ K 8 6
                          ♣ A 10 5
              ♠ K
              ♡ 10 7               N
              ◇ Q J 9 4 3      W       E
              ♣ K 9 8 6 3          S
```

South	West	North	East
		1NT[1]	2◇[2]
2♡	2NT[3]	3♡	Pass
Pass	4♣[3]	Pass	5◇
5♡	Double	All Pass	

[1] strong no-trump (15–17)
[2] Astro convention, showing spades and another suit
[3] see below

West leads the ♠K, which holds the trick.

East's 2◇ showed five spades and at least four cards in another suit with values for an opening bid (just). 2♡ was competitive and 2NT showed a good hand. 3♡ continued the barrage. With ten cards in the minors, we bid on with 4♣, asking partner to pass or correct depending on which minor was his second suit. Partner, viewing his hand as pretty powerful and expecting us to hold short spades, leapt to game; even if this was the wrong bid, South came to the rescue with 5♡ which allowed us to double and settle for a definite positive score.

Surveying dummy after the king of spades holds the first trick, it seems that South has made a pretty good bid for we should make 5◇ losing just a heart and a club (South is likely to hold just ♡AJxxxx and out). To beat this we will need to take 5♡ three off (for +500 against +400 for 5◇). Can we do it?

A

Dealer North. Love All. Duplicate Pairs.

```
                    ♠ Q J 2
                    ♡ K Q 6 2
                    ◇ K 8 6
                    ♣ A 10 5
    ♠ K                              ♠ A 10 9 8 6
    ♡ 10 7          N                ♡ 4
    ◇ Q J 9 4 3   W   E              ◇ A 10 7 2
    ♣ K 9 8 6 3     S                ♣ Q J 2
                    ♠ 7 5 4 3
                    ♡ A J 9 8 5 3
                    ◇ 5
                    ♣ 7 4
```

South	West	North	East
		1NT¹	2◇²
2♡	2NT³	3♡	Pass
Pass	4♣³	Pass	5◇
5♡	Double	All Pass	

¹strong no-trump (15–17)
²Astro convention, showing spades and another suit
³see previous page

West leads the ♠K, which holds the trick.

There are four easy tricks – one diamond, two spades and a spade ruff –
and we might hope for a fifth in clubs. But to get our spade ruff we have
to play to partner's ace of diamonds without establishing dummy's king,
otherwise declarer will discard his club loser. Leading the queen of
diamonds won't do the trick because declarer can simply duck. Our only
chance is to try to convey our predicament to partner by doing something
odd and the oddest card available is the nine of diamonds. What can this
mean?

It is not fourth highest and it cannot be top of nothing (nor second top).
Hopefully partner will stare at the nine of diamonds for a long time and
finally play the ten, allowing us to score +500 for a top.

When desperate for partner to do something out of the ordinary try
conveying this message to him by finding an odd play of your own.

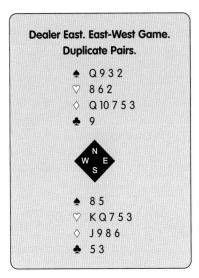

Dealer East. East-West Game.
Duplicate Pairs.

♠ Q 9 3 2
♡ 8 6 2
◇ Q 10 7 5 3
♣ 9

N
W E
S

♠ 8 5
♡ K Q 7 5 3
◇ J 9 8 6
♣ 5 3

South	West	North	East
			1♣[1]
2♣[2]	Double[3]	2NT	Pass
3◇	Double	4◇	Double
All Pass			

[1]strong club, sixteen or more points but says nothing about clubs.
[2]two suits of the same colour
[3]positive, seven or more points; once again this bid says nothing about clubs

West leads the ◇2 to East's ◇A; there follows the ◇K and ◇4
(on which West discards the ♣2 and ♣A).

We are the culprits this time! Each time somebody plays the Strong Club against us, we feel it necessary to bid on anything and of course, we have the necessary gadgets to confuse.

Here we show two suits of the same colour. Partner expects us to hold at least five cards in each suit and is willing to pre-empt to the three level in either spades or diamonds (depending on which colour of suit we hold). We show the red suits by bidding our lowest suit, 3◇, and now West's second double is for take-out. Partner raises the stakes even higher by bidding 4◇ and East decides that a penalty double is called for and there the auction ends. Eventful and quite possibly expensive.

With trumps drawn can we restrict the damage?

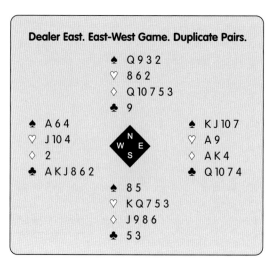

Dealer East. East-West Game. Duplicate Pairs.

```
                    ♠ Q 9 3 2
                    ♡ 8 6 2
                    ◇ Q 10 7 5 3
                    ♣ 9
♠ A 6 4                              ♠ K J 10 7
♡ J 10 4           N                 ♡ A 9
◇ 2            W         E            ◇ A K 4
♣ A K J 8 6 2      S                 ♣ Q 10 7 4
                    ♠ 8 5
                    ♡ K Q 7 5 3
                    ◇ J 9 8 6
                    ♣ 5 3
```

South	West	North	East
			1♣[1]
2♣[2]	Double[3]	2NT	Pass
3◇	Double	4◇	Double
All Pass			

[1] strong club, sixteen or more points but says nothing about clubs.
[2] two suits of the same colour
[3] positive, seven or more points; once again this bid says nothing about clubs

West leads the ◇2 to East's ◇A; there follows the ◇K and ◇4
(on which West discards the ♣2 and ♣A).

The aim is to go no more than three down: –500 against an easy –630 for 3NT + 1 or of course 6♣ which should actually make with an overtrick for –1390. We have six obvious losers – two trumps, two spades, one club and the ace of hearts – so we cannot afford to lose another one; importantly this means keeping our heart losers down to one.

It looks best to lead up to the ♡KQ twice, hoping that East holds the ace. But, we cannot succeed if we have to play a club before establishing our hearts, because if the opponents switch to spades they will remove the last trump from our hand, creating a third spade loser. Our only hope is to play East for ace doubleton in hearts, so we follow our heart to the king with a small heart from both hands and now East's ace is played on air. We just lose the six expected tricks, escaping for only –500 and a complete top.

Each of the following (South) hands made the asterisked bids in their respective auctions – what are the names of the conventions that they were using?

(1)
- ♠ K Q 8 4 3 2
- ♡ 6 3 2
- ◇ J 7 4
- ♣ 6

South	West	North	East
2◇*	Pass	2♡	Pass
2♠	All Pass		

(2)
- ♠ 10 7 4 2
- ♡ 3 2
- ◇ J 5 3 2
- ♣ 7 3 2

South	West	North	East
		1♠	Pass
3♠*	All Pass		

(3)
- ♠ 7 2
- ♡ 3 2
- ◇ 6 5 4
- ♣ Q J 8 6 4 3

South	West	North	East
	2♡¹	Double	Pass
2NT*	Pass	3♣	All Pass

¹weak two

(4)
- ♠ 7 3
- ♡ A K Q 10 5 4 3
- ◇ 6 3 2
- ♣ 4

South	West	North	East
		1NT¹	Pass
4♣*	Pass	4♡	All Pass

¹strong no-trump (15–17)

(5)
- ♠ A J 9 4 3
- ♡ 2
- ◇ K Q J 9 6
- ♣ 7 4

South	West	North	East
			2♡¹
3♡²	4♡	4NT³	5♡
Double*	Pass	6♠	All Pass

¹weak two
²Michaels Cue Bid
³Blackwood

A

(1) The Multi-coloured Two Diamonds (or simply 'Multi') – Multi-coloured describes the various meanings the bid can have. The most common usage is as a three-way bid showing either: (a) a weak two in a major (as here); (b) a strong two in a minor; or (c) a strong balanced hand.

Opener shows his colours on the second round: rebidding (or passing his partner's response) in a major to show (a); rebidding in a minor to show (b); and rebidding in no-trumps to show (c).

(2) Bergen Raises – North's opening bid shows five cards and in the Bergen system, a raise to three of the major is weak, really only carrying the message of four-card trump support. It is based on the principle of bidding to the level of one's fit – nine cards: so bid for nine tricks. (Why? Because usually the opponents will have a fit elsewhere and by bidding quickly to our level, it makes it difficult for them to bid).

To show better four-card raises to 3♠, Bergen uses the bids of 3♣ and 3♢ artificially, the former showing 6–9 points and the latter 10–12.

(3) Lebensohl – South uses the 2NT relay to show a weak hand with clubs. With a stronger hand, he would bid 3♣ direct. The convention basically requires partner to bid 3♣ and then the 2NT bidder clarifies his hand. Here, with clubs, he passes; with diamonds, he would bid 3♢. The convention can also be used to show invitational hands and other types such as different balanced hands.

(4) South African Texas – 4♣ is a transfer to hearts and 4♢ would have been a transfer to spades. With interest in slam, opener can bid the intermediate suit. The convention is used for two reasons – to allow the stronger hand to be declarer and also to differentiate between weak and intermediate hands with six- or seven-card suits.

(5) PODI – Pass = 0 aces, Double = 1 ace (sometimes also called DIPO); or DOPE – Double = Odd number of aces, Pass = Even number of aces.

These conventions deal with intervention over Blackwood. Here, if we responded to Blackwood by the usual step method, we would have to go beyond the safety of 5♠ just to show one ace.

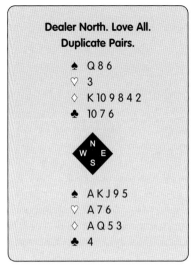

Dealer North. Love All.
Duplicate Pairs.

♠ Q 8 6
♡ 3
◇ K 10 9 8 4 2
♣ 10 7 6

♠ A K J 9 5
♡ A 7 6
◇ A Q 5 3
♣ 4

South	West	North	East
		2♣	Pass
2♠	Pass	3♠	Pass
4◇	Pass	4♡	Pass
4NT	Pass	5♣	Pass
5◇	Pass	6◇	Pass
6♠	All Pass		

West leads the ♡2.

We are playing a rather strange system today, which includes a Multi 2♣
bid. Similar to a Multi 2◇, this bid carries a variety of meanings. In this
case, it meant that North held either a weak two-bid in diamonds (as he
does, just about) or various very strong hands (an Acol 2♣).

2♠ was forcing for one round and North sensibly supported. 4◇ and
4♡ were cue bids. 4NT was Roman Key-Card Blackwood (for spades); 5♣
showed no aces and now 5◇ asked about the trump queen. North sensibly
offered the choice of slams, showing a good diamond suit and the queen of
spades when he bid 6◇, but we were not giving up on the higher-scoring
major suit, it being Duplicate Pairs. After all of that we have reached a very
good slam.

How should we play?

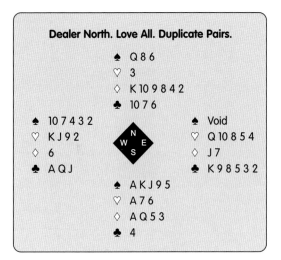

Dealer North. Love All. Duplicate Pairs.

South	West	North	East
		2♣	Pass
2♠	Pass	3♠	Pass
4◇	Pass	4♡	Pass
4NT	Pass	5♣	Pass
5◇	Pass	6◇	Pass
6♠	All Pass		

West leads the ♡2.

This hand is a matter of avoiding temptation. It seems so natural to ruff a heart in dummy but here that would lead to disaster. We must count our tricks: five spades, six diamonds and the ace of hearts add up to twelve, hence no need for a ruff to make our contract.

But this is Duplicate, so should we not be striving for overtricks? First we must ask ourselves how many other people will reach slam on this deal? The answer is probably none as the most likely auction is Pass–Pass–1♠–Pass–2♠–Pass–4♠.

The only worry is a 5-0 trump split, and we must aim to make our slam when this occurs. Win the ace of hearts and cash the ace of spades on which East shows out. Now you are in a position to finesse the eight of spades, cash the queen and cross back to hand with a diamond with fingers crossed. West does not ruff so you are home.

You open the score slip to see that indeed you were the only pair in slam – certainly a worthwhile safety play.

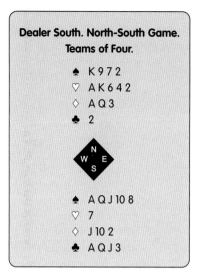

Dealer South. North-South Game. Teams of Four.

North
♠ K 9 7 2
♡ A K 6 4 2
◇ A Q 3
♣ 2

South
♠ A Q J 10 8
♡ 7
◇ J 10 2
♣ A Q J 3

South	West	North	East
1♠	2NT[1]	3◇[2]	Pass
4♣[3]	Pass	4NT[4]	Pass
5♠	Pass	5NT	Pass
6♣	Pass	6♠	All Pass

[1]unusual, showing at least ten cards in the minor suits; could be very weak
[2]shows support for spades
[3]cue-bid
[4]Roman Key Card Blackwood; 5♠ showed two (of five) aces and the trump queen

West leads the ♠3.

A well-judged auction. Once North had heard positive noises from South (South would have simply rebid spades with a bad hand), he was ready to use Blackwood. 5NT was a general grand-slam enquiry; 6♣ was natural, showing high cards in the suit and this put North off bidding 7♠.

On the bidding, West having shown the minors, seven looks a good prospect, but we are not there, so let us concentrate on the small slam.

Can we find the best line of play?

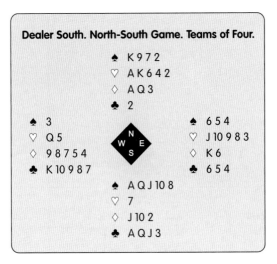

Dealer South. North-South Game. Teams of Four.

	♠ K 9 7 2	
	♡ A K 6 4 2	
	◇ A Q 3	
	♣ 2	
♠ 3		♠ 6 5 4
♡ Q 5		♡ J 10 9 8 3
◇ 9 8 7 5 4		◇ K 6
♣ K 10 9 8 7		♣ 6 5 4
	♠ A Q J 10 8	
	♡ 7	
	◇ J 10 2	
	♣ A Q J 3	

South	West	North	East
1♠	2NT¹	3◇²	Pass
4♣³	Pass	4NT⁴	Pass
5♠	Pass	5NT	Pass
6♣	Pass	6♠	All Pass

¹unusual, showing at least ten cards in the minor suits; could be very weak
²shows support for spades
³cue-bid
⁴Roman Key-Card Blackwood; 5♠ showed two (of five) aces and the trump queen

West leads the ♠3.

We have nine top tricks with extras available from ruffs or from either minor. A cross-ruff looks like a reasonable option, but this may fail when West has a singleton heart, since he would be able to ruff the king of hearts. A better line is to play to develop tricks in the minor suits and combine that with ruffs: it is not unreasonable to place West with at least one of the minor-suit kings for his unusual 2NT overcall.

Win the spade in hand, lead a heart to dummy (catering for a void in the West hand) and then play the ace of clubs and run the queen of clubs. If it loses, then surely the diamond finesse will work; if it wins, then we have enough tricks for our contract: two club ruffs, two hearts, ace of diamonds and five trumps in our hand.

After trick one, all our trumps are high, so there is no danger of an overruff.

Q

Dealer South. Game All.

♠ K 10 4 2
♡ Q 7 2
◇ A Q
♣ K Q 6 5

♠ A 9
♡ A K 5
◇ J 9 5 4
♣ 10 8 4 3

South	West	North	East
1♠	Pass	2NT¹	Pass
3♡¹	Pass	3♠¹	Pass
3NT¹	Pass	4♣¹	Pass
4◇¹	Pass	4♠	All Pass

¹see below

West leads the ♡A, on which partner plays the ♡3.

Here is a chance to see some science in action. South's 1♠ is a five-card major and 2NT is the Maxi Raise showing four-card trump support and fourteen or more points. 3♡ shows one of three hand shapes – 5-4-2-2, 5-4-4-0 or 6-3-2-2. 3♠ is a relay and 3NT shows four clubs. 4♣ is another relay and 4◇ shows a balanced hand type – 5-2-2-4. North, with a lack of first-round controls, signs off.

Now we have seen dummy, we need to form a plan.

Dealer South. Game All.

	♠ K 10 4 2	
	♡ Q 7 2	
	◊ A Q	
	♣ K Q 6 5	

♠ A 9		♠ 6 3
♡ A K 5	N W E S	♡ 10 9 8 6 3
◊ J 9 5 4		◊ 10 8 6 3 2
♣ 10 8 4 3		♣ 7

	♠ Q J 8 7 5	
	♡ J 4	
	◊ K 7	
	♣ A J 9 2	

South	West	North	East
1♠	Pass	2NT[1]	Pass
3♡[1]	Pass	3♠[1]	Pass
3NT[1]	Pass	4♣[1]	Pass
4◊[1]	Pass	4♠	All Pass

[1]see previous page

West leads the ♡A, on which partner plays the ♡3.

This is quite simple, although without the bidding it would have been a different prospect. Here all we need to do is listen to the opponents' bidding (and their explanations!) and add up the clubs. South has shown four, there are four in dummy and four in our hand, this just leaves one for partner. Holding first-round control in trumps we should be able to engineer a ruff for partner.

Switch to a club, which declarer will win and play a trump. We quickly take our ace, cash the king of hearts and fire back a club for partner to ruff – one down.

We can thank our opponents for this one. Scientific bidding can get great results, but it can also draw a very pretty picture for the defence, as long as they are willing to listen.

Bernard Magee's Bridge Quiz Book

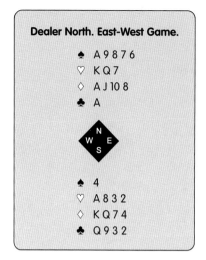

Dealer North. East-West Game.

♠ A 9 8 7 6
♡ K Q 7
◇ A J 10 8
♣ A

♠ 4
♡ A 8 3 2
◇ K Q 7 4
♣ Q 9 3 2

South	West	North	East
		1♣¹	Pass
1◇²	Pass	1♠	Pass
2NT²	Pass	3◇²	Pass
4♣²	Pass	4NT²	Pass
5♡²	Pass	7◇	All Pass

¹Precision strong club, showing sixteen or more points
²see below

West leads the ◇9.

North opens with the linchpin of the Precision system, the strong club. South's bid is ostensibly negative and North responds naturally, but South's jump rebid shows that his original 1◇ bid was the 'impossible negative' which describes hands of 4-4-4-1 shape. In this case the 2NT bid specifies a spade singleton. North can now see that the diamond suit is the best fit and there is a good chance of slam. He bids 3◇, which enquires about the strength of the diamond suit. South's response shows two of the top three honours.

A good solid trump suit, now all we need is the ace of hearts. Thus, North rolls out the Blackwood convention (this time Five-Ace Blackwood) and South's response shows two 'aces' (ace of hearts and king of diamonds). The grand slam is by no means a certainty, but North was feeling adventurous.

Well, after all that, can we make all thirteen tricks?

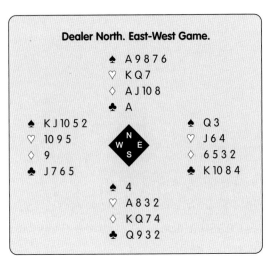

Dealer North. East-West Game.

South	West	North	East
		1♣[1]	Pass
1◇[2]	Pass	1♠	Pass
2NT[2]	Pass	3◇[2]	Pass
4♣[2]	Pass	4NT[2]	Pass
5♡[2]	Pass	7◇	All Pass

[1]Precision strong club, showing sixteen or more points
[2]see previous page

West leads the ◇9.

We need to ruff three spades in hand, which will be enough if spades split 4-3, but if spades break badly our only chance will be a 3-3 heart break. We must time the play carefully to cater for this extra chance.

Win the ten of diamonds, cash the ace of spades and ruff a spade. It looks obvious to use the ace of clubs as the first entry back to dummy, but it is better to use a heart. Now we lead the third spade and East throws a heart. We know we need a 3-3 heart break because spades have broken badly. So we ruff the third spade, re-enter dummy with a heart and ruff a fourth spade. Back to dummy with the ace of clubs, draw trumps and cash the two hearts for a well-earned thirteen tricks.

If we use the ace of clubs as a first entry, when we try to cross to dummy with a heart after the third spade ruff, East will ruff, having discarded all his hearts. It is just a question of timing.

Q BRIDGE TRIVIA

1. What is 'ASPTRO'?

2. Which is the odd one out: Baby, Greek, Byzantine or Roman?

3. Where in the world did the Precision system originate?

4. What can be Colourful, Michaels, Western, Wilfred and Cappalletti?

5. What is usually the 'fifth ace'?

6. Which two suits are labelled the 'pointed' suits?

7. What does CRASH (a defence to the Strong Club) stand for?

8. What is a Limit Bid?

9. Which place is not the name of a convention: San Francisco, Copenhagen, Chicago, Sahara or Texas?

10. What can be Alpha, Beta, Gamma or Delta?

11. What is Josephine?

12. What does MUD stand for?

13. What is a Splinter bid?

14. What can be Rusinow, Roman or Journalist?

15. What is the difference between a 'Peter' and an 'Echo'?

16. With which convention might you use Ogust rebids?

17. What (in bridge) is Canapé?

18. What do Arno, Roman, Schenken, Ultimate and Precision all have in common?

19. How did the ASTRO convention (a defence to 1NT) get its name?

20. Which is the odd one out: Multi-coloured, Flannery, Neapolitan, Swiss or Mexican?

ANSWERS TO BRIDGE TRIVIA

1. A defence to 1NT (a mixture of Astro and Aspro): 2♣ shows hearts and another suit and 2◇ shows spades and another suit.

2. Greek. The others are forms of Blackwood.

3. Asia. Charles Wei, the system's creator, was from China, although the first national team to use precicion was Taiwan.

4. Cue bids.

5. The king of trumps.

6. Diamonds and spades.

7. Colour, RAnk, SHape (round or pointed), referring to pairs of suits of the given description.

8. A bid which limits the point count of a hand within a small range (at most four points).

9. Chicago – it is a form of Rubber Bridge.

10. Asking bids, in the Precision system.

11. A bid of 5NT as a Grand-Slam Force asking partner how many of the top three trump honours are held.

12. Middle Up Down; a type of lead style from three small cards.

13. A bid which shows shortage (one or less cards in the suit bid) as well as support for partner's suit. Often used opposite a one-level, major-suit opening, a double jump shift would be the splinter bid (eg 1♠–Pass–4♣ would show a singleton club and four or more spades with game values).

14. Leads.

15. Nothing! Both refer to the playing of a high card followed by a lower card in a suit. The first term is British, the second American.

16. Weak-two bids.

17. Bidding a shorter suit before a longer one.

18. They are club systems (based on an artificial 1♣ bid).

19. From the names of its inventors: Allinger, STern and ROsler.

20. Swiss. All of the others can be 2◇ openings.

Chapter 9

Brain Teasers

For those who enjoy self-torture, we finish with a few extra-difficult questions designed to tickle the grey cells. The trivia section deals with some of the more difficult aspects of play.

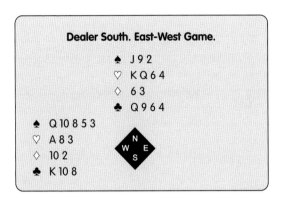

Dealer South. East-West Game.

North
- ♠ J 9 2
- ♡ K Q 6 4
- ◇ 6 3
- ♣ Q 9 6 4

West
- ♠ Q 10 8 5 3
- ♡ A 8 3
- ◇ 10 2
- ♣ K 10 8

South	West	North	East
1◇	Pass	1♡	Pass
3NT	All Pass		

West leads the ♠5 to the ♠9, ♠K and ♠A.

An inauspicious start. Declarer then starts playing diamonds: ace, king, queen, jack … (he has six). Plan your discards. Dummy throws a heart and two clubs before the last diamond.

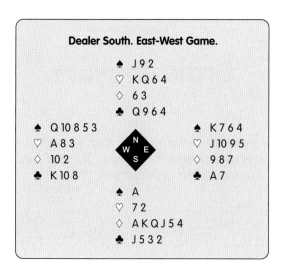

Dealer South. East-West Game.

	♠ J 9 2	
	♡ K Q 6 4	
	◊ 6 3	
	♣ Q 9 6 4	

♠ Q 10 8 5 3		♠ K 7 6 4
♡ A 8 3		♡ J 10 9 5
◊ 10 2		◊ 9 8 7
♣ K 10 8		♣ A 7

	♠ A	
	♡ 7 2	
	◊ A K Q J 5 4	
	♣ J 5 3 2	

South	West	North	East
1◊	Pass	1♡	Pass
3NT	All Pass		

West leads the ♠5 to the ♠9, ♠K and ♠A.

The most important thing to note is that if declarer holds the ace of clubs 3NT is cold – six diamonds, ace of spades, ace of clubs and an easily established heart trick. Why would South bid 3NT with so few points? Because that is where he wanted to play; with seven top tricks he needed little from partner, the ace and king of hearts would have been nice, to give nine top tricks. It is basically a 'gambling' bid.

Declarer is going to have to hold on to dummy's major-suit cards, and so we, needing only one more trick (ace of hearts, ace and king of clubs and queen of spades), do best to hold on to our clubs, hoping to score a third trick there. We must keep all of our clubs, and then if dummy comes down to a singleton queen we will be able to underlead our king to partner's ace and a club back would finesse declarer and take the contract down. Thus in the diagram below dummy will not discard a club unless we do.

This is the position before declarer leads his last diamond:

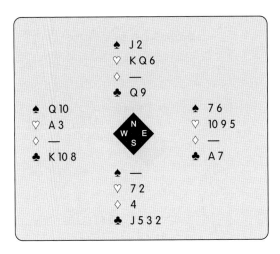

As long as we discard a major-suit card, we can take the contract off, but notice how much more difficult it is if we discard a spade. Now when dummy also discards a spade East MUST keep his second spade – otherwise we can only take four tricks. Hence when we discard a spade, we put partner under pressure, not a good thing. So our best play is to discard a heart. Dummy has to discard a heart too and now when we win the ace of hearts we are in charge and must play the king of clubs and then a small club to East's ace, who should be able to see the correct play now: a heart to lock declarer in dummy and force a lead into our spade tenace, one down.

Whenever possible, if you can see a winning line of defence, make sure you take control. A spade discard gives partner a chance to go wrong.

Dealer South. Love All.

♠	K 9 8 3
♡	9 5
◇	Q 7 6
♣	K 10 6 3

```
      N
   W     E
      S
```

♠	A 4
♡	7 6 3
◇	A K 8 5 3 2
♣	A 9

South	West	North	East
1◇	1♡	Double	2♡
3◇	Pass	3♡¹	Pass
4◇	Pass	5◇	All Pass

¹no-trump probe, asking for a heart stop.

West leads the ◇J.

North has done a lot of work in the auction and his actions turn out to be right as he has guided us to a very reasonable contract. Unfortunately, though, the defence are also on good form.

We win the lead in dummy and lead a heart, but East pops in with the ten and leads another trump (West discarding a heart). Another heart runs to the jack, nine and ace and as expected a third trump comes back (West discarding the queen of hearts) and we have to say goodbye to our ruff in dummy. Is there any other hope?

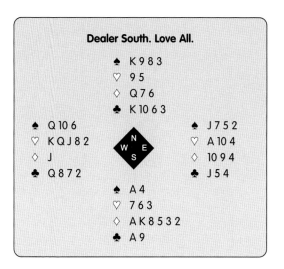

Dealer South. Love All.

```
                    ♠ K 9 8 3
                    ♡ 9 5
                    ◇ Q 7 6
                    ♣ K 10 6 3
   ♠ Q 10 6                      ♠ J 7 5 2
   ♡ K Q J 8 2       N           ♡ A 10 4
   ◇ J            W     E        ◇ 10 9 4
   ♣ Q 8 7 2         S           ♣ J 5 4
                    ♠ A 4
                    ♡ 7 6 3
                    ◇ A K 8 5 3 2
                    ♣ A 9
```

South	West	North	East
1◇	1♡	Double	2♡
3◇	Pass	3♡¹	Pass
4◇	Pass	5◇	All Pass

¹no-trump probe, asking for a heart stop.

West leads the ◇J.

A very nice defence, but unfortunately for East-West, in order to stop declarer ruffing in dummy, East had to play both his top hearts, thus isolating the heart guard with West and giving declarer a glimmer of hope.

At first sight, it seems that our only chance is to squeeze West in a black suit and hearts – clubs seems more likely for we only need him to hold ♣QJ. But there are actually chances for a guard squeeze if West holds two of the three spades higher than the nine or three of the four clubs higher than the six. We start by cashing our black aces and then lead a trump:

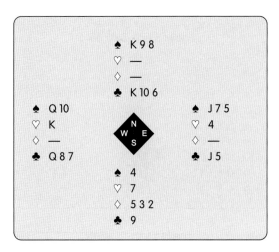

This exerts pressure on West. He has to hold on to a heart and does not want to shorten his longer black suit, for then we can simply establish a trick by ruffing. In this case, he discards the ten of spades, and this opens up the extra chance of a ruffing finesse; the guard squeeze has worked.

We discard a club from dummy and follow with a spade to the king, which draws the queen from West. Now we lead the nine of spades; if East does not cover we throw our heart: if East does cover we ruff and return to dummy via the king of clubs to cash the eight of spades.

In all cases, we should discard in the opposite suit to which West discards. Here, if West lets go a club, dummy throws a spade and we play the king of clubs and ruff a club, finally returning to dummy with the king of spades to cash the established club.

Note, had West started with three clubs and four spades, then had the clubs been Q87 the guard squeeze would have worked again, allowing us to take a ruffing finesse against the jack of clubs in the endgame.

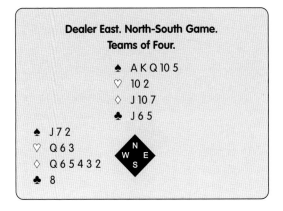

Dealer East. North-South Game.
Teams of Four.

♠ A K Q 10 5
♡ 10 2
◇ J 10 7
♣ J 6 5

♠ J 7 2
♡ Q 6 3
◇ Q 6 5 4 3 2
♣ 8

South	West	North	East
			3♣
6♡	All Pass		

West leads the ♣8 which goes to the ♣5, ♣Q and ♣A.

This auction occurred at the tail end of a teams match when East-West were desperate, 30 IMPs down and needing some swings. East's opening clearly gave South a real bidding problem, which he solved by taking a pot at slam. He seems to have found a good dummy.

Sitting West, we not unreasonably lead our singleton club, which goes to the five, queen and ace. Declarer now leads the ace of hearts. What is our plan?

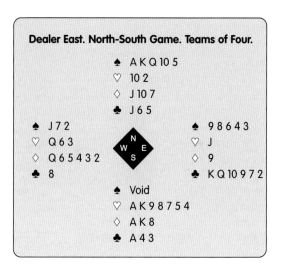

Dealer East. North-South Game. Teams of Four.

```
                    ♠  A K Q 10 5
                    ♡  10 2
                    ♢  J 10 7
                    ♣  J 6 5
    ♠  J 7 2                          ♠  9 8 6 4 3
    ♡  Q 6 3           N              ♡  J
    ♢  Q 6 5 4 3 2   W   E            ♢  9
    ♣  8               S              ♣  K Q 10 9 7 2
                    ♠  Void
                    ♡  A K 9 8 7 5 4
                    ♢  A K 8
                    ♣  A 4 3
```

South	West	North	East
			3♣
6♡	All Pass		

West leads the ♣8 which goes to the ♣5, ♣Q and ♣A.

East certainly was trying to make things happen! But his bid did make things awkward for North-South. As a defender, after this auction, one rather expects the contract to make with the sight of four or five tricks in dummy.

Partner has suggested he holds the ♣KQ (otherwise he would not have played the queen, establishing the jack). So what does South need for his bidding? ♠xx ♡AKxxxx ♢Axx ♣Ax? Surely this is not enough? And yet even without the king of diamonds, because we have no clubs left, declarer will be able to make his slam. Do not even start to think that partner might hold the ace of diamonds!

Basically this contract is going to make unless declarer is void in spades. Unlikely, but our only chance. So, what if declarer does have a void spade?

If West wins the third round of trumps he will be forced to give dummy an entry. How can we avoid winning the third round of trumps? We throw the six beneath the ace (not the queen yet, or declarer can reach table with ten). Underneath the king of hearts goes the queen and now declarer is helpless; we have the lowest trump remaining, and so he has to lose one diamond and two clubs.

Q

Dealer North. Love All.

South	West	North	East
1♠	Pass	4♣	Pass
?			

We open 1♠ and partner responds with a Splinter bid, showing at most one club and four-card trump support with at least game values (12–15 points). What should we bid on the following hands?

(1)
- ♠ K Q 5 3 2
- ♡ A 7 6
- ◇ 3 2
- ♣ K J 4

(2)
- ♠ K Q 5 3 2
- ♡ A 7 6
- ◇ 3 2
- ♣ A 9 4

(3)
- ♠ K Q 5 3 2
- ♡ A K 7
- ◇ 3 2
- ♣ K J 4

(4)
- ♠ K Q 5 3 2
- ♡ A K 7
- ◇ 3 2
- ♣ 9 8 4

(5)
- ♠ K Q 10 3 2
- ♡ A K 7 3
- ◇ 2
- ♣ A 9 4

Suppose partner holds:

♠ A J 7 6
♡ Q J 8 2
◇ A K 5 4
♣ 6

(1) 4♠ – A minimum hand and not a good fit. ♣KJ4 are wasted values opposite a shortage.

(2) 4♡ – Very suitable indeed: no wasted values in clubs, not very strong, but worth co-operating with a first round cue-bid (showing the ace of hearts). Partner can try Blackwood* now, three of the five aces along with the queen of spades is enough for slam.

(3) 4♡ – Strong hand, but not ideal opposite a club singleton. Still, we should be positive and cue bid 4♡. Blackwood* from partner again (two aces and the queen of trumps). He now knows that slam is on one of two finesses or perhaps better so is worth a shot. It turns out to be a cold slam!

(4) 4♡ – A weak hand, but no wasted values and good controls, again show the first-round control. Blackwood* once again steers the partnership to slam. (Notice how little the king and jack of clubs were worth in the last hand).

(5) 4NT – Super-strong and ideal, so we can ask for aces*. After a two-ace response further enquiries should get us to 7♠.

*The Blackwood referred to above is Roman Key-Card Blackwood: 4NT asks for aces as usual but the king of trumps is counted as a fifth ace. The responses are:

5♣ 0 or 3 aces
5◇ 1 or 4 aces
5♡ 2 or 5 aces without the trump queen
5♠ 2 or 5 aces with the trump queen

After 5♣/5◇ the next suit up asks about the trump queen and so one can always find out how good the trump suit is as well as discovering the number of aces.

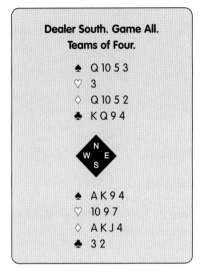

Dealer South. Game All.
Teams of Four.

♠ Q 10 5 3
♡ 3
◇ Q 10 5 2
♣ K Q 9 4

♠ A K 9 4
♡ 10 9 7
◇ A K J 4
♣ 3 2

South	West	North	East
1♠	Double	4♠	All Pass

West leads the ◇9.

North made short work of getting to game, not allowing his opponents to interfere. We are in the right place, but West has fired a warning shot, suggesting things may not be as easy as they seem.

A 4-1 trump break may be on the cards, and West may well have pinpointed his partner's short suit. Can we cope with a 4-1 break and a singleton diamond?

A

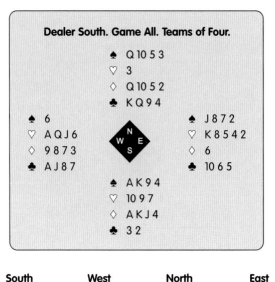

Dealer South. Game All. Teams of Four.

```
                 ♠ Q 10 5 3
                 ♡ 3
                 ◇ Q 10 5 2
                 ♣ K Q 9 4
   ♠ 6                            ♠ J 8 7 2
   ♡ A Q J 6          N           ♡ K 8 5 4 2
   ◇ 9 8 7 3      W       E       ◇ 6
   ♣ A J 8 7          S           ♣ 10 6 5
                 ♠ A K 9 4
                 ♡ 10 9 7
                 ◇ A K J 4
                 ♣ 3 2
```

South	West	North	East
1♠	Double	4♠	All Pass

West leads the ◇9.

No! We cannot cope with a singleton diamond and 4-1 trump break, but we can try to make it difficult for the defence.

Essentially we cannot afford to play anything before we draw three rounds of trumps, because the defence will be able to negotiate two aces and two ruffs. But if we draw three rounds of trumps, we cannot quite manage ten tricks ourselves – after winning the third trump in hand with the nine (ace of spades, queen of spades and then a finesse) we lead a club to the king which wins, but now what?

The best shot is to play the queen of spades, ace of spades and a small club… This puts West under some pressure. How does he know what is going on? If he goes up with the ace, he might be making things easy for you, but if he ducks, we can draw a third round of trumps and lead another club. We are now one step ahead and can get home because we have established our second club trick.

Of course, having seen the layout, the best play is a club at trick two making it even more difficult for West to see what is going on, but partner would be disappointed if he found us going off with trumps 3-2, which could be the case if there was a singleton diamond.

Dealer South. East-West Game.
Rubber Bridge.

♠ Q 8 2
♡ A 4 3 2
♦ A K 6
♣ 6 3 2

♠ A K J 10 7 5
♡ Void
♦ Q 5 3 2
♣ A J 10

South	West	North	East
1♠	Pass	2♡	Pass
3♠	Pass	4NT	Pass
6♠	All Pass		

West leads the ♡J.

Not the prettiest auction. North's 4NT bid was awful; with three losing clubs there was no security in 5♠. But South's leap to 6♠ was perhaps not unreasonable. In any event, the slam seems to have plenty of chances.

What is the best way to utilise all our cards?

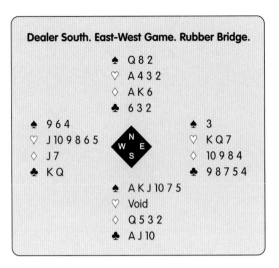

Dealer South. East-West Game. Rubber Bridge.

```
                    ♠ Q 8 2
                    ♡ A 4 3 2
                    ◇ A K 6
                    ♣ 6 3 2
    ♠ 9 6 4                          ♠ 3
    ♡ J 10 9 8 6 5      N            ♡ K Q 7
    ◇ J 7           W       E        ◇ 10 9 8 4
    ♣ K Q              S             ♣ 9 8 7 5 4
                    ♠ A K J 10 7 5
                    ♡ Void
                    ◇ Q 5 3 2
                    ♣ A J 10
```

South	West	North	East
1♠	Pass	2♡	Pass
3♠	Pass	4NT	Pass
6♠	All Pass		

West leads the ♡J.

It is important to notice that we must not discard from hand at trick one (a diamond would give up on being able to ruff the fourth round or on a 3-3 split, whereas a club would give up on the double finesse). It is best to leave this decision until later. So ruff the lead in hand and draw trumps (West holding three), finishing in dummy. Now, a club finesse runs to West's queen. Ruff the heart return (we still do not know what to do), cash the last trump throwing a club, and then cash the queen, king and ace of diamonds. Disappointingly, West shows out on the third diamond, but we continue with our plan. We cash the ace of hearts and discard the diamond from hand. Now with just two cards left we play a small club from dummy and East follows small.

Think for a moment: we know East's last card is the thirteenth diamond. So there is no point finessing because West definitely holds the king of clubs. We hop up with the ace of clubs and are pleasantly surprised by the fall of the king. Of course, had we not known East's last card we would have taken the finesse as our original plan.

This play is called a show-up squeeze; because East is forced to hold on to his diamond, the club position is 'shown up'.

Dealer South. Love All.
Teams of Four

South	West	North	East
1♣[1]	2♣[2]	Double[3]	4♣[4]
Double	Pass	Pass	?

[1]strong club
[2]both majors
[3]positive, seven or more points
[4]equal length in both majors with a club feature

We, as East, hold:

♠ Q 6 3 2
♡ Q J 10 2
◇ 7 6
♣ A 5 4

We are not playing in a regular partnership, but before the start of play, we agreed a defence to the Strong Club and wrote it on our convention cards. The auction thus far has been rather protracted and partner writhed a little when we alerted his 2♣ bid. North enquired about its meaning and we stated clearly that it showed length in both major suits; partner seemed to be distinctly unhappy with this explanation. When you bid 4♣, partner did not alert it, but South asked what the bid meant and begrudgingly your partner gave the explanation given in (4) above. After South's double there was another pause before partner passed. Perhaps he really has clubs?

What do you bid?

A It is always difficult to behave ethically when there is a bad bidding misunderstanding, but partner should really have alerted 4♣ even though he has got a long club suit and that is all.

Anyway, at least he eventually explained our agreement which states that 4♣ shows a hand with equal length in the majors willing to support to the four level.

We cannot and must not pass. Partner, when he did have his bid, might pass with 5-5 in the majors and be asking us to bid our better (more solid) major. Thus we must continue bidding naturally and call 4♡.

Note, if the bidding had been 1♣–2♣–Double–4♣–Pass–Pass–Double–?, now we can pass the double, for partner's pass has clearly shown up the misunderstanding to both sides in the auction. Due to his failure to alert and basic discomfort, it is obvious there has been a misunderstanding this time, but there has been no such information gleaned from the bidding and thus we have to bid on naturally.

Only ever take advantage of your partner's bidding, not his actions. If he fails to alert a bid, play on as if he had alerted it.

Here, although 4♣ doubled is not a disaster we are not allowed to play there, for on another day during the same sequence, if partner had alerted 4♣, sat quietly and bid confidently we would not even dream of passing 4♣ doubled!!

Partner was used to playing all two-level bids as weak bids with a six card suit. He held:

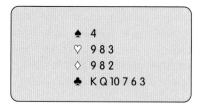

♠ 4
♡ 9 8 3
♢ 9 8 2
♣ K Q 10 7 6 3

and simply bid 5♣ over 4♡, which was doubled. He escaped for just three down and −500 which was not such a disaster, with North-South having an easy game.

Q

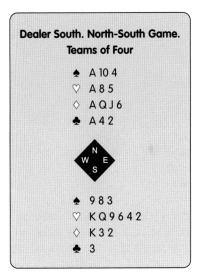

Dealer South. North-South Game.
Teams of Four

♠ A 10 4
♡ A 8 5
◇ A Q J 6
♣ A 4 2

♠ 9 8 3
♡ K Q 9 6 4 2
◇ K 3 2
♣ 3

South	West	North	East
2♡[1]	Pass	2NT[2]	Pass
4♣[3]	Pass	4◇[4]	Pass
4♡	Pass	4♠[4]	Pass
5◇[4]	Pass	6♡	Pass
Pass	Double	All Pass	

[1]weak two, good six-card suit, 6–9 points
[2]strong, agreeing hearts as trumps
[3]splinter bid, showing shortage in clubs
[4]cue-bids

West leads the ♠K.

Here we go again! How often do we agonize over such sequences, only to hear the dreaded double at the end. This was certainly a well-bid slam. Note, how useful it can be to play constructive weak twos – a good six-card suit and 6–9 points. So often in these aggressive times, pairs play a nebulous pre-emptive strategy which leaves constructive bidding by the wayside.

Here 2NT agreed hearts and 4♣ showed shortage. This splinter bid was ideal opposite North's club holding and slam was tidily bid. All going swimmingly until West stepped in.

Sometimes the double can be a help rather than a hindrance. Any ideas?

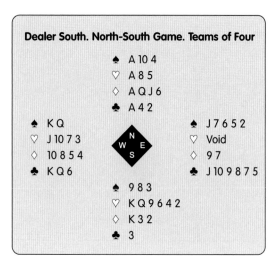

Dealer South. North-South Game. Teams of Four

	♠ A 10 4	
	♡ A 8 5	
	◇ A Q J 6	
	♣ A 4 2	
♠ K Q		♠ J 7 6 5 2
♡ J 10 7 3		♡ Void
◇ 10 8 5 4		◇ 9 7
♣ K Q 6		♣ J 10 9 8 7 5
	♠ 9 8 3	
	♡ K Q 9 6 4 2	
	◇ K 3 2	
	♣ 3	

South	West	North	East
2♡¹	Pass	2NT²	Pass
4♣³	Pass	4◇⁴	Pass
4♡	Pass	4♠⁴	Pass
5◇⁴	Pass	6♡	Pass
Pass	Double	All Pass	

¹weak two, good six-card suit, 6-9 points
²strong, agreeing hearts as trumps
³splinter bid, showing shortage in clubs
⁴cue bids

West leads the ♠K.

Unfortunately, our bidding seems to have come to little. We would usually play the ace of hearts first to cope with J10xx in East's hand, but after West's double, we play a small heart from dummy and unsurprisingly East discards. Our only chance appears to be an endplay on West. We are unable to shorten our trumps to less than his, so we will be forced to use an exit card to endplay him into leading trumps. This will require him to hold exactly KQ doubleton of spades. Furthermore, we will also need his shape in the minors to be the same as dummy – four diamonds and three clubs. If this is so, we should be able to strip him of his minor-suit cards and put him on lead with the queen of spades. A slim hope, but our only chance!

Play a low trump from hand and West perforce inserts the ten. Now we win with the ace and strip West's hand: ace of clubs, club ruff, diamond, club ruff, and cash the rest of the diamonds. This is the position:

Bernard Magee's Bridge Quiz Book

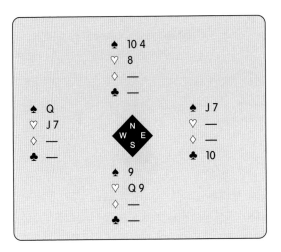

Finally we exit with a spade and West, who has to win with the queen, is forced to lead from ♡J7 into South's ♡Q9. Thus South makes the last two tricks and with them his slam. Well bid and well played! Maybe West will have learned two valuable lessons!

Dealer East. Game All.
Teams of Four

♠ 10 6 5
♡ A 6 5 4
◇ K 4 2
♣ A 7 4

```
        N
    W       E
        S
```

♠ A K 4 3 2
♡ 2
◇ A 7 3
♣ K 9 3 2

South	West	North	East
			2♡¹
2♠	Pass	3♡²	Pass
4♠	Double	All Pass	

¹weak with hearts and a minor
²game try with spade support

West leads the ♡J.

3♠ in this auction would have been simply competitive, but the cue-bid shows a good hand with support and genuine invitational values. South was happy to accept.

We have plenty of high cards, so it seems that we must be up against a rather nasty trump break, but at least we know.

Can we use this information to our advantage?

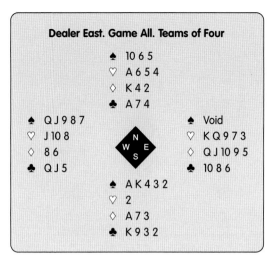

Dealer East. Game All. Teams of Four

	North		
	♠ 10 6 5		
	♡ A 6 5 4		
	◇ K 4 2		
	♣ A 7 4		

West: ♠ Q J 9 8 7 ♡ J 10 8 ◇ 8 6 ♣ Q J 5

East: ♠ Void ♡ K Q 9 7 3 ◇ Q J 10 9 5 ♣ 10 8 6

South: ♠ A K 4 3 2 ♡ 2 ◇ A 7 3 ♣ K 9 3 2

South	West	North	East
			2♡¹
2♠	Pass	3♡²	Pass
4♠	Double	All Pass	

¹weak with hearts and a minor
²game try with spade support

West leads the ♡J.

It is unlikely that East started with more than five hearts – these nuisance bids are designed for specifically five in the major and anything from four to six cards in the minor suit. So it seems as though we should be able to ruff two hearts safely if need be. One worry might be that West holds a singleton club, but we cannot cope with this, so we assume that our high cards are standing up – that gives us seven tricks. Three more tricks are required and trumps seem the only way to supply them; as suggested two are available by ruffing hearts but where is the third one coming from? The answer is: from the endgame.

Let us try ruffing hearts. We win the ace of hearts and ruff a heart. Cash the ace of diamonds (under which East throws the queen), king of diamonds and ruff another heart. Now the king of clubs (West throws his jack beneath this) and then the ace of clubs which swallows West's queen. Now simply exit with a non-trump card and you will be able to get home. In this position, we already have seven tricks.

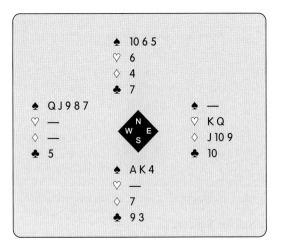

For example: try a diamond. If East wins, West will have to ruff the next trick and lead the queen of spades. But South can win and simply exit with a non-trump card once again, endplaying West.

Suppose West had ruffed his partner's diamond winner and then led a club back to East. When East now leads a heart, South must ruff with the ace of spades (West being forced to underruff) and lead his last club. If West ruffs high he is endplayed, having to lead away from a single honour. If he ruffs low, North wins the tenth trick with an overruff.

Or West might ruff the diamond and lead the queen of spades. South wins this and exits with a club. Now, when East wins and leads a heart, South can discard and West perforce ruffs and is endplayed.

Q   BRIDGE TRIVIA

1. What is a Merrimac Coup?

2. What does 'to strip' mean in bridge?

3. Which is the odd one out: Double, Compound, Guard, Square, or Trump?

4. What is a Psychic Bid?

5. What is a Vienna Coup?

6. What is a Suicide Squeeze?

7. Which one of the following has NOT been a member of a victorious Bermuda Bowl team: Gabriel Chagas, Eric Rodwell, Zia Mahmood, Giorgio Belladonna, or Bob Hamman?

8. What does 'to rectify the count' mean?

9. What is an Alcatraz Coup?

10. What two geometrical shapes can be associated with squeeze names?

11. What is a Scissors Coup?

12. There are two plays known as 'disappearing trump tricks', when a defender's seemingly certain trump winner vanishes – what are they?

13. Which is the odd one out: Bath, Morton's Fork, Idiot, Robert or Chicken?

14. What is a Falsecard?

15. What might BLUE have to do with a squeeze?

16. What is a Safety Play?

17. North holds ♠AK1074 opposite ♠8653. When he cashes the ace, East follows with the jack. What principle might North apply?

18. Vinje, Scanian, Smith and Upside-down are all examples of what?

19. What is 'to pin'?

20. What is a Simple Squeeze?

A ANSWERS TO BRIDGE TRIVIA

1. The sacrifice of a high card in order to knock out an entry in an opponent's hand.

2. To remove easy exit cards from an opponent, so that he might be endplayed and have no safe card to exit with.

3. Square – the others are types of squeeze.

4. A bid that appears to make no logical sense according to the convention played. They are made to confuse the auction, and thus put off the opponents from finding their best contract.

5. An unblocking play in preparation for a squeeze.

6. A squeeze inflicted by a defender on his partner.

7. Zia Mahmood.

8. To lose a trick or tricks in order to reach a squeeze position (usually with just one loser left).

9. An illegal play in which declarer deliberately fails to follow suit so as to see which card his left-hand opponent will play. When he sees it, he announces, with humble apologies, that he mistakenly revoked, and so he replaces his card and now with the required knowledge to make his contract, proceeds!

10. Hexagon and Octagon.

11. A play to cut the opponents' communications.

12. Devil's Coup and Smother Play.

13. Chicken – the others are names of bridge coups.

14. The play of a non-normal card in order to deceive an opponent.

15. It is a mnemonic for the successful operation of a squeeze: B = Busy; L = Loser; U = Upper; E = Entry.

16. A play which is made to increase the safety of the contract against adverse distributions, often at the expense of overtricks.

17. The Principle of Restricted Choice.

18. Methods of signalling.

19. To play a high card, under which a slightly lower-ranking card falls from right-hand opponent.

20. A squeeze which acts against one opponent in two suits.